MATH KINDERGARTEN
Teacher's Guide

Author:
Carol Bauler, B.A.

Revision Editor:
Alan Christopherson, M.S.

Media Credits:
Page 63: © belander, iStock, Thinkstock.

Alpha Omega
PUBLICATIONS

**804 N. 2nd Ave. E.,
Rock Rapids, IA 51246-1759**

MATH
KINDERGARTEN

LIFEPAC® Overview

MATH SCOPE & SEQUENCE

KINDERGARTEN

Lessons 1–40	Lessons 41–80	Lessons 81–120	Lessons 121–160
Directions – right, left, high, low, etc.	**Directions** – right, left, high, low, etc.	**Directions** – right, left, high, low, etc.	**Directions** – right, left, high, low, etc.
Comparisons – big, little, alike, different	**Comparisons** – big, little, alike, different	**Comparisons** – big, little, alike, different	**Comparisons** – big, little, alike, different
Matching	**Matching**	**Matching**	**Matching**
Cardinal Numbers – to 9	**Cardinal Numbers** – to 12	**Cardinal Numbers** – to 19	**Cardinal Numbers** – to 100
Colors – red, blue, green, yellow, brown, purple	**Colors** – orange	**Colors** – black, white	**Colors** – pink
Shapes – circle, square, rectangle, triangle	**Shapes** – circle, square, rectangle, triangle	**Shapes** – circle, square, rectangle, triangle	**Shapes** – circle, square, rectangle, triangle
Number Order	**Number Order**	**Number Order**	**Number Order**
Before and After	**Before and After**	**Before and After**	**Before and After**
Ordinal Numbers – to 9th	**Ordinal Numbers** – to 9th	**Ordinal Numbers** – to 9th	**Ordinal Numbers** – to 9th
Problem Solving	**Problem Solving**	**Problem Solving**	**Problem Solving**
	Number Words – to nine	**Number Words** – to nine	**Number Words** – to nine
	Addition – to 9	**Addition** – multiples of 10	**Addition** – to 10 and multiples of 10
		Subtraction – to 9	**Subtraction** – to 10
		Place Value	**Place Value**
		Time/Calendar	**Time/Calendar**
			Money
			Skip Counting – 2s, 5s, 10s
			Greater/Less Than

MATH SCOPE & SEQUENCE

	Grade 1	Grade 2	Grade 3
UNIT 1	**NUMBER ORDER, ADD/SUBTRACT** • Number order, skip count • Add, subtract to 9 • Story problems • Measurements • Shapes	**NUMBERS AND WORDS TO 100** • Numbers and words to 100 • Operation symbols: +, –, =, >, < • Add and subtract • Place value and fact families • Story problems	**ADD/SUB TO 18 AND PLACE VALUE** • Digits, place value to 999 • Add and subtract • Linear measurements • Operation symbols: +, –, =, ≠, >, < • Time
UNIT 2	**ADD/SUBTRACT TO 10, SHAPES** • Add, subtract to 10 • Number words • Place value • Patterns, sequencing, estimation • Shapes	**ADD/SUBTRACT AND EVEN/ODD** • Numbers and words to 200 • Add, subtract, even and odd • Skip count 2s, 5s, and 10s • Ordinal numbers, fractions, and money • Shapes	**CARRYING AND BORROWING** • Fact families, patterns, and fractions • Add and subtract with carrying and borrowing • Skip count 2s, 5s, 10s • Money, shapes, lines • Even and odd
UNIT 3	**FRACTIONS, TIME, AND SYMBOLS** • Number sentences • Fractions • Story problems • Time and the = symbol • Oral directions	**ADD WITH CARRYING TO THE 10'S PLACE** • Add with carrying to the 10's place • Subtract • Flat shapes, money, a.m./p.m. • Rounding to the 10's place • Standard measurements	**FACTS OF ADD/SUB AND FRACTIONS** • Add 3 numbers w/ carrying • Coins, weight, volume, a.m./p.m. • Fractions • Skip count 3s, subtract w/ borrowing • Oral instructions
UNIT 4	**ADD TO 18, MONEY, MEASUREMENT** • Add to 18 • Skip count, even and odd • Money • Shapes and measurement • Place value	**NUMBERS/WORDS TO 999, AND GRAPHS** • Numbers and words to 999 • Addition, subtraction, and place value • Calendar • Measurements and solid shapes • Making change	**ROUND, ESTIMATE, STORY PROBLEMS** • Place value to 9,999 • Rounding to the 10's and estimating • Add and subtract fractions • Roman numerals • 1/4 inch
UNIT 5	**COLUMN ADDITION AND ESTIMATION** • Add three 1–digit numbers • Ordinal numbers • Time and number lines • Estimation and charts • Fractions	**ADD/SUBTRACT TO THE 100'S PLACE** • Data and bar graphs and shapes • Add and subtract to the 100's place • Skip count 3s and place value to the 100's place • Add fractions • Temperature	**PLANE SHAPES AND SYMMETRY** • Number sentences • Rounding to the 100's and estimation • Perimeter and square inch • Bar graph, symmetry, and even/odd rules • Temperature
UNIT 6	**NUMBER WORDS TO 99** • Number words to 99 • Add two 2–digit numbers • Symbols: > and < • Fractions • Shapes	**SUBTRACT WITH BORROWING FROM 10'S** • Measurements • Time and money • Subtract w/ borrowing from the 10's place • Add and subtract fractions • Perimeter	**MULTIPLICATION, LINES, AND ANGLES** • Add and subtract to 9,999 • Multiples and multiplication facts for 2 • Area and equivalent fractions • Line graphs, segments, and angles • Money
UNIT 7	**COUNT TO 200, SUBTRACT TO 12** • Number order and place value • Subtract to 12 • Operation signs • Estimation and time • Graphs	**ADD WITH CARRYING TO THE 100'S PLACE** • Add with carrying to the 100's place • Fractions as words • Number order in books • Rounding and estimation	**ADD/SUB MIXED NUMBERS, PROBABILITY** • Multiplication facts for 5 and missing numbers • Add and subtract mixed numbers • Subtract with 0s in the minuend • Circle graphs • Probability
UNIT 8	**ADD/SUBTRACT TO 18** • Addition, subtract to 18 • Group counting • Fractions • Time and measurements • Shapes	**VOLUME AND COIN CONVERSION** • Addition, subtraction, and measurements • Group counting and "thinking" answers • Convert coins • Directions – north, south, east, and west • Length and width	**MEASUREMENTS AND MULTIPLICATION** • Multiplication facts for 3 & 10, multiples of 4 • Convert units of measurement • Decimals and directions • Picture graphs and missing addends • Length and width
UNIT 9	**SENSIBLE ANSWERS** • Fact families • Sensible answers • Subtract 2–digit numbers • Add three 2–digit numbers	**AREA AND SQUARE MEASUREMENT** • Area and square measurement • Add three 2–digit numbers with carrying • Add coins and convert to cents • Fractions and quarter–inches	**MULT, METRICS, AND PERIMETER** • Add and subtract whole numbers, fractions, and mixed numbers • Standard measurements and metrics • Operation symbols • Multiplication facts for 4
UNIT 10	**ADDITION AND SUBTRACTION REVIEW** • Addition, subtraction, and place value • Directions – north, south, east, and west • Fractions • Patterns	**CARRYING AND BORROWING REVIEW** • Rules for even and odd numbers • Round numbers to the 100's place • Digital clocks and sensible answers • Add three 3–digit numbers	**PROBABILITY, UNITS, AND SHAPES** • Addition and subtraction • Rounding to the 1,000's place and estimating • Probability, equations, and parentheses • Perimeter and area • Multiplication facts for 2, 3, 4, 5, and 10

MATH SCOPE & SEQUENCE

Grade 4	Grade 5	Grade 6	
WHOLE NUMBERS AND FRACTIONS • Naming whole numbers • Naming fractions • Sequencing patterns • Numbers to 1,000	**PLACE VALUE, ADDITION, AND SUBTRACTION** • Place value • Rounding and estimating • Addition • Subtraction	**WHOLE NUMBERS AND ALGEBRA** • Whole numbers and their properties • Operations and number patterns • Algebra	UNIT 1
MULTIPLYING WHOLE NUMBERS • Operation symbols • Multiplication — 1-digit multipliers • Addition and subtraction of fractions • Numbers to 10,000	**MULTIPLYING WHOLE NUMBERS AND DECIMALS** • Multiplying whole numbers • Powers • Multiplying decimals	**DATA ANALYSIS** • Collecting and describing data • Organizing data • Displaying and interpreting data	UNIT 2
SEQUENCING AND ROUNDING • Multiplication with carrying • Rounding and estimation • Sequencing fractions • Numbers to 100,000	**DIVIDING WHOLE NUMBERS AND DECIMALS** • One–digit divisors • Two–digit divisors • Decimal division	**DECIMALS** • Decimal numbers • Multiplying and dividing decimal numbers • The metric system	UNIT 3
LINES AND SHAPES • Plane and solid shapes • Lines and line segments • Addition and subtraction • Multiplication with carrying	**ALGEBRA AND GRAPHING** • Expressions • Functions • Equations • Graphing	**FRACTIONS** • Factors and fractions • The LCM and fractions • Decimals and fractions	UNIT 4
DIVISION AND MEASUREMENTS • Division – 1-digit divisors • Families of facts • Standard measurements • Number grouping	**MEASUREMENT** • The metric system • The customary system • Time • Temperature	**FRACTION OPERATIONS** • Adding and subtracting fractions • Multiplying and dividing fractions • The customary system	UNIT 5
DIVISION, FACTORS, AND FRACTIONS • Division — 1-digit divisors with remainders • Factors and multiples • Improper and mixed fractions • Equivalent fractions	**FACTORS AND FRACTIONS** • Factors • Equivalent fractions • Fractions	**RATIO, PROPORTION, AND PERCENT** • Ratios • Proportions • Percent	UNIT 6
WHOLE NUMBERS AND FRACTIONS • Multiplication — 2-digit multipliers • Simplifying fractions • Averages • Decimals in money problems • Equations	**FRACTION OPERATIONS** • Like denominators • Unlike denominators • Multiplying fractions • Dividing fractions	**PROBABILITY AND GEOMETRY** • Probability • Geometry: Angles • Geometry: Polygons	UNIT 7
WHOLE NUMBERS AND FRACTIONS • Division — 1-digit divisors • Fractions and unlike denominators • Metric units • Whole numbers: +, –, x, ÷	**DATA ANALYSIS AND PROBABILITY** • Collecting data • Analyzing data • Displaying data • Probability	**GEOMETRY AND MEASUREMENT** • Plane figures • Solid figures	UNIT 8
DECIMALS AND FRACTIONS • Reading and writing decimals • Adding and subtracting mixed numbers • Cross multiplication • Estimation	**GEOMETRY** • Geometry • Classifying plane figures • Classifying solid figures • Transformations • Symmetry	**INTEGERS AND TRANSFORMATIONS** • Integers • Integer operations • Transformations	UNIT 9
ESTIMATION, CHARTS, AND GRAPHS • Estimation and data gathering • Charts and graphs • Review numbers to 100,000 • Whole numbers: +, –, x, ÷	**PERIMETER, AREA, AND VOLUME** • Perimeter • Area • Surface area • Volume	**EQUATIONS AND FUNCTIONS** • Equations • More equations and inequalities • Functions	UNIT 10

MATH SCOPE & SEQUENCE

	Grade 7	Pre-algebra Grade 8	Algebra 1 Grade 9
UNIT 1	INTEGERS • Adding and Subtracting Integers • Multiplying and Dividing Integers • The Real Number System	THE REAL NUMBER SYSTEM • Relationships • Other Forms • Simplifying	VARIABLES AND NUMBERS • Variables • Distributive Property • Definition of signed numbers • Signed number operations
UNIT 2	FRACTIONS • Working with Fractions • Adding and Subtracting Fractions • Multiplying and Dividing Fractions	MODELING PROBLEMS IN INTEGERS • Equations with Real Numbers • Functions • Integers • Modeling with Integers	SOLVING EQUATIONS • Sentences and formulas • Properties • Solving equations • Solving inequalities
UNIT 3	DECIMALS • Decimals and Their Operations • Applying Decimals • Scientific Notation • The Metric System	MODELING PROBLEMS WITH RATIONAL NUMBERS • Number Theory • Solving Problems with Rational Numbers • Solving Equations and Inequalities	PROBLEM ANALYSIS AND SOLUTION • Words and symbols • Simple verbal problems • Medium verbal problems • Challenging verbal problems
UNIT 4	PATTERNS AND EQUATIONS • Variable Expressions • Patterns and Functions • Solving Equations • Equations and Inequalities	PROPORTIONAL REASONING • Proportions • Percents • Measurement/Similar Figures	POLYNOMIALS • Addition of polynomials • Subtraction of polynomials • Multiplication of polynomials • Division of polynomials
UNIT 5	RATIOS AND PROPORTIONS • Ratios, Rates, and Proportions • Using Proportions • Fractions, Decimals, and Percents	MORE WITH FUNCTIONS • Solving Equations • Families of Functions • Patterns	ALGEBRAIC FACTORS • Greatest common factor • Binomial factors • Complete factorization • Word problems
UNIT 6	PROBABILITY AND GRAPHING • Probability • Functions • Graphing Linear Equations • Direct Variation	MEASUREMENT • Angle Measures and Circles • Polygons • Indirect Measure	ALGEBRAIC FRACTIONS • Operations with fractions • Solving equations • Solving inequalities • Solving word problems
UNIT 7	DATA ANALYSIS • Describing Data • Organizing Data • Graphing Data and Making Predictions	PLANE GEOMETRY • Perimeter and Area • Symmetry and Reflections • Other Transformations	RADICAL EXPRESSIONS • Rational and irrational numbers • Operations with radicals • Irrational roots • Radical equations
UNIT 8	GEOMETRY • Basic Geometry • Classifying Polygons • Transformations	MEASURE OF SOLID FIGURES • Surface Area • Solid Figures • Volume • Volume of Composite Figures	GRAPHING • Equations of two variables • Graphing lines • Graphing inequalities • Equations of lines
UNIT 9	MEASUREMENT AND AREA • Perimeter • Area • The Pythagorean Theorem	DATA ANALYSIS • Collecting and Representing Data • Central Tendency and Dispersion • Frequency and Histograms • Box–and–Whisker Plots • Scatter Plots	SYSTEMS • Graphical solution • Algebraic solutions • Determinants • Word problems
UNIT 10	SURFACE AREA AND VOLUME • Solids • Prisms • Cylinders	PROBABILITY • Outcomes • Permutations and Combinations • Probability and Odds • Independent and Dependent Events	QUADRATIC EQUATIONS AND REVIEW • Solving quadratic equations • Equations and inequalities • Polynomials and factors • Radicals and graphing

MATH SCOPE & SEQUENCE

Geometry Grade 10	Algebra 2 Grade 11	Pre-calculus Grade 12	
A MATHEMATICAL SYSTEM • Points, lines, and planes • Definition of definitions • Geometric terms • Postulates and theorems	**SETS, STRUCTURE, AND FUNCTION** • Properties and operations of sets • Axioms and applications • Relations and functions • Algebraic expressions	**RELATIONS AND FUNCTIONS** • Ordered-pair numbers • Algebra of functions	UNIT 1
PROOFS • Logic • Reasoning • Two-column proof • Paragraph proof	**NUMBERS, SENTENCES, & PROBLEMS** • Order and absolute value • Sums and products • Algebraic sentences • Number and motion problems	**FUNCTIONS** • Linear functions • Second-degree functions • Polynomial and special functions • Complex numbers	UNIT 2
ANGLES AND PARALLELS • Definitions and measurement • Relationships and theorems • Properties of parallels • Parallels and polygons	**LINEAR EQUATIONS & INEQUALITIES** • Graphs • Equations • Systems of equations • Inequalities	**RIGHT TRIANGLE TRIGONOMETRY** • Solving a right triangle • Unit circle and special angles • Reciprocal functions and identities • Radian measure	UNIT 3
CONGRUENCY • Congruent triangles • Corresponding parts • Inequalities • Quadrilaterals	**POLYNOMIALS** • Multiplying polynomials • Factoring • Operations with polynomials • Variations	**GRAPHING AND INVERSE FUNCTIONS** • Graphing • Sinusoidal functions • Inverse trigonometric functions • Trigonometric equations	UNIT 4
SIMILAR POLYGONS • Ratios and proportions • Definition of similarity • Similar polygons and triangles • Right triangle geometry	**RADICAL EXPRESSIONS** • Multiplying and dividing fractions • Adding and subtracting fractions • Equations with fractions • Applications of fractions	**ANALYTIC TRIGONOMETRY** • Trigonometric identities • Addition formulas • Double- and half-angle formulas • Products and sums	UNIT 5
CIRCLES • Circles and spheres • Tangents, arcs, and chords • Special angles in circles • Special segments in circles	**REAL NUMBERS** • Rational and irrational numbers • Laws of Radicals • Quadratic equations • Quadratic formula	**TRIGONOMETRIC APPLICATIONS** • Trigonometry of oblique triangles • Vectors	UNIT 6
CONSTRUCTION AND LOCUS • Basic constructions • Triangles and circles • Polygons • Locus meaning and use	**QUADRATIC RELATIONS & SYSTEMS** • Distance formulas • Conic sections • Systems of equations • Application of conic sections	**POLAR COORDINATES** • Polar equations • Complex numbers	UNIT 7
AREA AND VOLUME • Area of polygons • Area of circles • Surface area of solids • Volume of solids	**EXPONENTIAL FUNCTIONS** • Exponents • Exponential equations • Logarithmic functions • Matrices	**QUADRATIC EQUATIONS** • Circles and ellipses • Parabolas and hyperbolas • Translations	UNIT 8
COORDINATE GEOMETRY • Ordered pairs • Distance • Lines • Coordinate proofs	**COUNTING PRINCIPLES** • Progressions • Permutations • Combinations • Probability	**COUNTING PRINCIPLES** • Probability • Combinations and permutations • Sequences, series, and induction	UNIT 9
GEOMETRY REVIEW • Proof and angles • Polygons and circles • Construction and measurement • Coordinate geometry	**ALGEBRA REVIEW** • Integers and open sentences • Graphs and polynomials • Fractions and quadratics • Exponential functions	**CALCULUS** • Limits • Slopes • Curves	UNIT 10

STRUCTURE OF THE KINDERGARTEN CURRICULUM

The Kindergarten program provides math readiness activities to support the LIFEPAC Math curriculum. Students move from very basic skills of size, shape, colors, and matching to learning beginning functions of addition, subtraction, and problem solving.

Kindergarten Math is conveniently structured to provide two student workbooks and a Teacher's Guide. The Teacher's Guide is designed to provide a step-by-step procedure that will help the teacher prepare for and present each lesson effectively. It is suggested that the 160 lessons be completed in a nine-month program.

A thorough study of the Curriculum Overview and teacher materials by the teacher before instruction begins is essential to the success of the student. The teacher should become familiar with expected skill mastery and understand how these grade-level skills fit into the overall skill development of the curriculum.

EVALUATION

Kindergarten students are generally not ready for formal test situations; however, some type of assessment of student progress is both appropriate and necessary. Although student evaluation may be done at any time, a thorough assessment should be done at the completion of each quarter's work (40 lessons). The results of the assessment will provide the teacher with a guide to the student's progress and an analysis of any of the student's weak areas. Student evaluation information is provided. Remember, the evaluation is not a test. The procedure is meant to help identify weaknesses before they become too great to overcome. Several days may be set aside for assessment or it may be integrated with regular daily work. Do not allow the student to tire of the activity or you will not achieve accurate results. Review is essential to success. Time invested in review where review is suggested will be time saved in correcting errors later.

GOAL SETTING AND SCHEDULES

Each school must develop its own schedule, because no one set of procedures will fit every situation. The following is an example of a daily schedule that gives an overall view of a typical day for a kindergarten student.

Possible Daily Schedule

8:30 – 8:40	Pledges, prayer, songs, devotions, etc.
8:40 – 9:00	Bible Reading, Memory Time, etc.
9:00 – 10:00	Language Arts *Learning to Read*
10:00 – 10:15	Break
10:15 – 11:00	Math
11:00 – 11:10	Review and Drill Assignments
11:10 – 11:15	Washroom Break
11:15 – 11:30	Activity (art, music, science, etc.)
11:30 – 11:45	Story Time
11:45 – 12:00	Clean Up
12:00	Dismissal

A key concept here is to be structured (have a plan), but be flexible enough to realize that some days will need to be adjusted to better fit the lesson and rate of learning. If more time is needed on a particular day to teach concepts, omit the noncritical activities and abbreviate each individual lesson while being careful that the concept is still covered. But be sure to leave in singing, story time, and other fun activities for transition between the more mentally taxing subjects. Because of the varying levels of maturity of children, they will grasp and retain the material at various times.

Long-range planning requires some organization. Because the traditional school year originates in the early fall of one year and continues to late spring of the following year, a calendar should be devised that covers this period of time. Approximate beginning and completion dates can be noted on the calendar as well as special occasions such as holidays, vacations, and birthdays. The 160 lessons in the kindergarten curriculum may be divided into four quarters of 40 lessons each. Starting at the beginning school date, mark off forty school days on the calendar and that will become the targeted completion date for the first quarter. Continue marking the calendar until you have established dates for the following three quarters or 120 lessons making adjustments for previously noted holidays and vacations.

TEACHING SUPPLEMENTS

The sample weekly lesson plan form is included in this section as teacher support material and may be duplicated at the convenience of the teacher.

WEEKLY LESSON PLANNER

Week of:

Monday	Subject	Subject	Subject	Subject

Tuesday	Subject	Subject	Subject	Subject

Wednesday	Subject	Subject	Subject	Subject

Thursday	Subject	Subject	Subject	Subject

Friday	Subject	Subject	Subject	Subject

WEEKLY LESSON PLANNER

Week of:

	Subject	Subject	Subject	Subject
Monday				
Tuesday	Subject	Subject	Subject	Subject
Wednesday	Subject	Subject	Subject	Subject
Thursday	Subject	Subject	Subject	Subject
Friday	Subject	Subject	Subject	Subject

INSTRUCTIONS FOR KINDERGARTEN MATH

The teacher instruction pages contain the objectives (concepts) to be taught in each lesson along with directions for teaching the corresponding student workbook pages. The activities included in the teaching page section that precede or follow the workbook assignments are used to reinforce or expand the concepts taught and are an integral part of the learning experience.

Students learn letter formation and penmanship in their reading and spelling programs. Because this is not a primary focus of math, the math curriculum begins immediately with the five-eighths separation between the bold writing lines along with the dotted guide line for lowercase letters.

Math is a subject that requires skill mastery, but skill mastery needs to be applied toward active student involvement. A list of materials/manipulatives is provided on each instruction page. A complete list for the entire *Kindergarten Math* curriculum is included in this section.

The *Introduction of Skills* that appears in this section is a quick reference guide for the teacher who may be looking for a rule or explanation that applies to a particular skill or to find where or when certain skills are introduced in the curriculum. The skills are grouped by Lessons (1–40, 41–80, 81–120, 121–160) for a convenient teacher reference during student evaluation.

MATERIALS/MANIPULATIVES

(As Required in Lesson Order)

- pencils
- plain and lined paper
- crayons—red, yellow, green, blue, brown, purple, orange, black, white, pink
- assorted objects
    - to illustrate big and little
    - for counting—beads, buttons, blocks, strips of cardboard, popsicle sticks, bottle caps, toothpicks, beans
- pictures illustrating big and little
- colored construction paper
- cardboard (cereal boxes work well)
- paste or glue
- scissors
- popsicle sticks may be substituted for counting strips (Lesson 9) (use marker to color sticks)
- paper or plastic bag
- pictures of objects to make sets
- empty metal or plastic containers of varying size—half cup to two cups
- string or yarn and clip (Lesson 93)
- pictures of 2 dogs and 2 cats, 9 pieces of candy, 3 drinking glasses (Lesson 107)
- calendar
- pennies and dimes
- chart of numbers to 50 (Lesson 131)
- chart of numbers to 99 (Lesson 143)

Number Symbol Cards and Fact Cards
- Two sets of each
    - one set with number on both sides or fact with answer
    - one set with number or fact on just one side—reverse side blank (second set will be used for games of concentration)

Use pieces of cardboard, two inches by three inches so that all cards are uniform in size and easily handled by the student.

1. Number symbols 1 through 12 (Lessons 30, 89)

2. Number picture cards (Lessons 32, 86—one set with reverse side blank)

3. Addition fact cards for 0 through 10 to a total of 10 (Lessons 59–60, 65, 71, 73–74, 105)

4. Number word cards for zero through ten (Lessons 86, 125)

5. Subtraction fact cards for 0 through 10 from up to 10 (Lessons 88, 91, 96, 125)

MATH K INTRODUCTION OF SKILLS: LESSONS 1–40

CONCEPT	LESSON	CONCEPT	LESSON
Before and after	33, 37–40	Ordinal (order) numbers	
		first – fifth	19
Colors		sixth – ninth	27
red, yellow, green, blue	1	Problem solving/critical thinking	
brown	7	concentration	30, 32
purple	23	estimate enough objects to make sets 1–5	22
Comparisons			
big, little, alike, different	2–5, 7–8, 11, 14–15, 18, 20–21, 25, 26, 34, 38	estimate enough objects to make sets 6–9	36
		can you select objects up to 9	35
Counting		Shapes	
1–5	9	circle, triangle, square, rectangle	3, 6, 7, 10–11, 15, 20–21, 23, 36–37, 39–40
6–9	25		
Following directions			
right, left, high, low, top, bottom, middle, above, below, inside, outside	1, 5, 14–15, 34	Write the number symbol	
		1–5	12
Matching	6–9, 11, 15, 18, 20–21, 26, 30, 33	6–9	28
Number order			
1–9	38–40		

MATH K INTRODUCTION OF SKILLS: LESSONS 41–80

CONCEPT	LESSON	CONCEPT	LESSON
Addition		Ordinal numbers	55, 57, 79
1–5 vertical	41	Problem solving/critical thinking	
1–9 vertical	48	concentration	44, 67
0–9 vertical	65	how many ways to	
0–9 horizontal as words	73	make a set 1–9	53
0–9 horizontal as		how many triangles	
numbers	77	from a square	69
Before and after	47, 79–80	how many facts from a	
Colors		number 1–9 (addition)	75
orange	59	Shapes	
Comparisons	44, 68, 79–80	circle, triangle, square,	
Counting		rectangle	46, 55, 60,
0–9	64		69–70, 79–80
10–12	76	Write numbers as words	
Following directions		one – five	61
right, left, high, low, top,		six – nine	62
bottom, middle, above,		zero	64
below, inside, outside	44, 68, 79–80	Write the number symbol	
Matching	60, 67, 70	0–9	64
Number(s) between	55, 59–60, 79–80	10–12	76
Number order			
0–9	67		
0–12	76		

MATH K INTRODUCTION OF SKILLS: LESSONS 81–120

CONCEPT	LESSON	CONCEPT	LESSON
Addition		Problem solving/critical thinking	
1–10 vertical	105	concentration	86, 95
add numbers to 10, 20, 30, 40, 50	110	estimation of number of objects	90
Before and after	87, 98, 105, 115	story problems	107
Colors		how many ways to make sets to 10	105
black	97	select objects up to 19	108
white	106	Shapes	
Comparisons		circle, triangle, square, rectangle	92, 98, 120
big, little, alike, different	90, 108, 116		
Counting		Subtraction	
13–19	101	1–5 vertical	81
Following directions		1–9 vertical	85
right, left, high, low, top, bottom, middle, above, below, inside, outside	89, 99, 100, 120	1–9 horizontal as words	96
		1–9 horizontal as numbers	96
Matching	89, 98, 120	Time/calendar	
Number(s) between	99	hour	93–94, 97, 115, 118, 119
Number order			
13–19	101	Write the number symbol	
Ordinal numbers	97	13–19	101
Place value			
1's and 10's	101		

MATH K INTRODUCTION OF SKILLS: LESSONS 121–160

CONCEPT	LESSON	CONCEPT	LESSON
Addition	130	Ordinal numbers	138
Before and after	131–132, 139, 140, 144, 147, 155, 157	Place value 1's and 10's	127
Colors pink	134	Problem solving/critical thinking concentration	121–122
Comparison big, little, alike, different	138, 157	story problems	146, 160
		patterns and sequencing	138, 157
Counting 20–50	126	Shapes circle, triangle, square, rectangle	138
51–99	143	Skip counting 10's	146
Following directions right, left, high, low, top, bottom, middle, above, below, inside, outside	156	2's	147
		5's	148
Greater than, less than 1–50	141,142	Subtraction 1–10 vertical	125
1–99	156, 160	Time/calendar hour	133, 140, 150, 159
Money pennies	135–136, 151–154, 158	half-hour	133–134, 139, 140, 150, 159
dimes	136, 152–154, 158	months	127, 134, 139, 140, 159
Number(s) between	123, 129–130, 155, 157	Write the number symbol 20–50	126
Number order 20–50	126	51–99	143
51–99	143		

MATH KINDERGARTEN

Lessons 1–10

LESSON 1

MATERIALS NEEDED

- pencils
- red, yellow, green, and blue crayons

Objectives:

1. To follow directions.

2. To set a realistic goal for the completion of work.

3. To learn about right, left, up, down, high, low, inside, outside, top, bottom.

4. To learn about the colors red, yellow, green, and blue.

Teaching Pages 1 and 2:

1. Turn to page 1. Point to the two dogs at the top of the page and say their names. Tell the children these two friends will be on many of their worksheets. Give the children time to look through the workbooks and to find the dogs.

My name is Sam!

My name is Jip!

What is your name?

My name is:

Teacher Check

Lesson 1 | **1**

2. Continue on page 1. Read what the dogs are saying. Point to the first line and read the words. Write each child's name on the line and ask him to read his name to you. Tell the children that their workbooks are divided into lessons and that together you will set a goal of completing one lesson each day. Show them that one lesson is usually two pages in their workbooks.

3. Introduce the red, yellow, green, and blue crayons to the children. Tell them that Sam and Jip have been playing with a big red ball and ask them to find the ball on the page. Compare the ball to a circle. Tell them they may color the ball using the red crayon. Instruct the children to always color in one direction and stay in the lines. Have the children complete the picture by adding green grass, a yellow sun, and a blue sky.

4. Introduce directions to the children by playing a game with them. Explain *right* and *left*. Ask them to hold up their *right* hands, put out their *left* legs, touch their *right* ears. Ask them to put their *right* hands on top of their heads. Ask them to put their *left* hands behind their backs. Continue this game using *right, left, up, down, high, low, top, bottom, inside, outside*. Have them turn to page 2. Ask them to find the *big* balls and the *little* balls and to identify the shape made by the *big* balls (heart). Tell them to color the *big* balls red. Have them use the yellow, green, and blue crayons to color the *little* balls. Ask them to identify the location of the *little* balls as they are coloring (*inside, outside,* on the *top*, on the *bottom*, to the *right*, to the *left*, and so on).

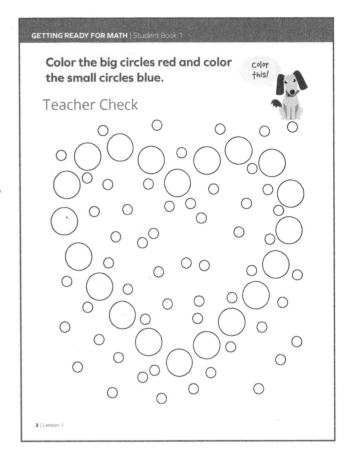

GETTING READY FOR MATH | Student Book 1

Color the big circles red and color the small circles blue.

color this!

Teacher Check

2 | Lesson 1

LESSON 2

MATERIALS NEEDED

- pencils
- pictures illustrating big and little (animals, children, toys, plants, houses, and so on) or objects illustrating big and little (two sizes of marshmallows, blocks, toy trucks, and so on)
- red, yellow, green, and blue crayons

Objectives:

1. To distinguish between big and little.

2. To use colors.

3. To identify the big object.

Teaching Pages 3 and 4:

1. Use the pictures or the collection of objects to begin a class discussion about big and little. Give each child an opportunity to touch and handle the pictures and objects.
   Ask: "Which of these items are alike?"
   "Which are different?"
   "How are they different?" "Which item is the big one?"
   Have the children look for big and little items in the classroom.

2. When you are sure that each child understands the concept of big and little, have the children open their workbooks to page 3. Read the title of the page to them. Discuss the meaning of the word *circle* and make sure each student understands how to draw one. Have the children look at the two cats in the middle of the page. Decide which cat is the big one and have the students draw a red circle around it. Look at the cats and the circles at the bottom of the page. Tell the students to circle the big cat and the big circle using a red crayon.

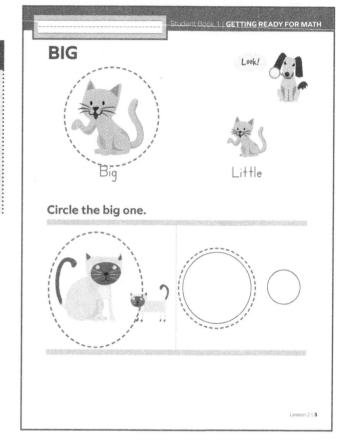

3. Turn to page 4. Ask the children to identify the color of the turtles (green), the pencil eraser (red), shoes (blue), and the braided hair (yellow). Ask them if they can find these colors anywhere else on the page. Have them look at each pair of items.
    Ask questions: "How are these two items alike?" (Both are turtles.) "How are these two items different?" (Different sizes) "Which item is the big one?" (Point) After doing this with each pair of items, read aloud the instructions at the top of the page. Have the children complete the page independently. Then, tell the children they may color the cats and circles on page 3 using any of the colors red, yellow, green, or blue.

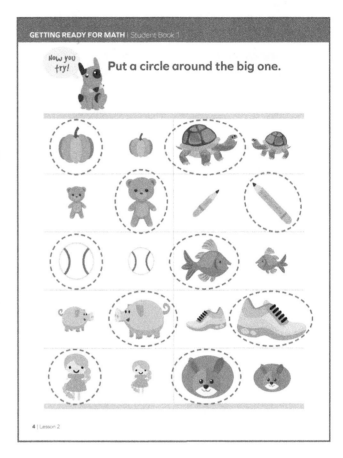

LESSON 3

MATERIALS NEEDED

- pencils
- red, yellow, green, and blue crayons
- construction paper
- cardboard
- paste or glue
- scissors

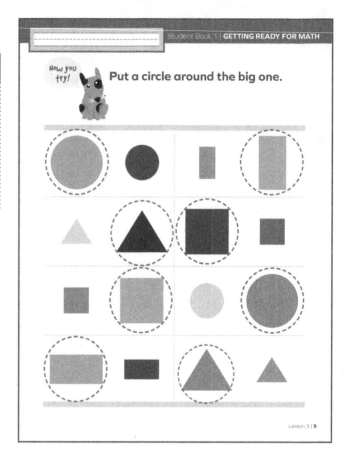

Objectives:

1. To learn about shapes.

2. To recognize circle, square, triangle, and rectangle.

3. To use colors.

4. To find the big object.

Teaching Page 5:

1. Talk to the students about shapes. Point out different shapes in the classroom. Tell them that shapes have names and that they will learn some of these names today. Have the students turn to page 5 in their workbooks. Ask them if they recognize any of the shapes. Tell them the names of the shapes and point out to them that the same shape can be in different sizes or directions. Ask them to find the red square, the blue circle, the yellow triangle, and the green rectangle. Have the children complete the page by circling the big object using their pencils.

2. Using construction paper or cardboard, help the children draw and cut out circles (use circular objects such as glasses for patterns), squares, triangles, and rectangles in different sizes and in different colors. Using a plain sheet of paper, show them how they can combine the shapes to form a picture. (Three circles can make a snowman; a rectangle and triangle can make a house.) Have them paste or glue their shapes onto the paper so that they can keep their picture. Use crayons to add grass, sun, clouds, sky, doors and windows to houses, and other objects to the picture. Be sure to refer to the shapes by their correct names as the children use them.

LESSON 4

MATERIALS NEEDED

- pencils
- pictures or objects illustrating big and little
- red, yellow, green, and blue crayons

Objectives:

1. To distinguish between big and little.

2. To use colors.

3. To identify the little object.

Teaching Pages 6 and 7:

1. Begin a discussion using the collection of objects. This time tell the children to select the little objects. Have the children open their workbooks to page 6. Point to the title and read it aloud. Have the children look at the two trees in the middle of the page. Decide which tree is the little one, and tell the children to circle it. Direct the children's attention to the two ducks at the bottom of the page. Instruct them to circle the little duck. Do the same with the caterpillars.

2. Turn to page 7. Ask the children if they recognize any colors. (Concentrate on red, yellow, blue, and green.) Next, point to the first box and ask: "How are these two objects alike?" (Both are flowers) "How are these two objects different?" (Different sizes) "Which object is the little one?" Do this with several pairs on the page. Be sure the students understand that they are following new directions. They are looking for the little object, not the big object. Have the children complete the page. Then tell the children they may color the ducks and caterpillars on page 6 using any of the colors red, yellow, green, or blue.

3. Using the collection of objects, play a game with the students. The teacher may select a big item and ask the students to find the small one; or, the students may select an item and must say if it is big or little. You may keep score and play the game until all of the objects are used.

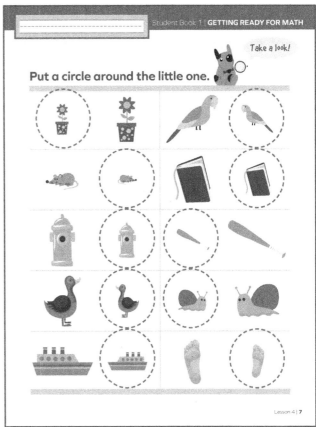

LESSON 5

MATERIALS NEEDED

- pencils
- red, yellow, green, and blue crayons

Objectives:

1. To follow directions.

2. To use colors.

3. To distinguish between big and little objects.

Teaching Pages 8 and 9:

1. Turn to page 8. Read the first set of instructions aloud, and have the students repeat these instructions. Be sure each child understands what he is to do. Allow the children to complete the exercise independently. Read the second set of instructions, and have the students complete the second exercise.

2. Play the game of right and left, up and down, above and below, behind and in front that was played in Lesson 1. Turn to page 9 and give these instructions: Use your *yellow* crayon to circle: 1) the *little* bird at the *top* of the page; and 2) the house that is on the *right* side.

3. Use your *red* crayon to circle: 3) the *little* bat that is under the *big* bat; and 4) the *big* boots that are *above* the socks.

4. Use your *green* crayon to circle: 5) the cake that is to the *left* of the *little* eggs; and 6) the socks that would fit *little* children.

5. Use your *blue* crayon to circle: 7) the horse that is above the *little* house; and 8) the *big* eggs at the *bottom* of the page.

6. You may repeat your instructions several times so that the children will feel successful in what they are doing. Allow them to finish by coloring the pictures on the page.

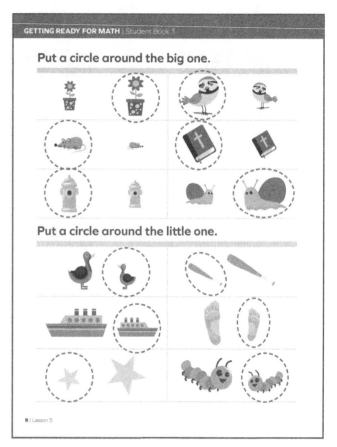

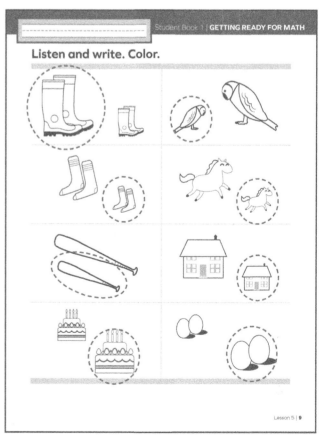

LESSON 6

MATERIALS NEEDED

- pencils
- pictures illustrating big and little (animals, children, toys, plants, houses, and so on)
- a large sheet of paper
- scissors
- paste or glue
- red, yellow, blue, and green construction paper

Objectives:

1. To match related objects one-to-one.

2. To use circles, triangles, squares, and rectangles.

Teaching Pages 10 and 11:

1. Explain to the class that today they will learn to match one-to-one. Ask the children what they think *match* means. Allow time for several answers. Explain that in the workbook to *match* means to draw a line between two objects so that the objects are connected.

2. Turn to page 10. Have the children point to the cowboy and cow in the first box and name the two objects. Call attention to the rope or line connecting or matching the two. Have the children point to the cowboy and cow in the second box. Call attention to the dotted line. Have the children draw the cowboy's rope along the dotted line. Emphasize that this line matches the cowboy to the cow. Repeat the same instructions with the fisherman and fish, the letter and the mailbox.

3. Give the children time to look at page 11. Ask what they notice about each of the pictures. Stop as soon as someone says the rope between the cowboy and cow is missing. Then ask if they can guess what they are supposed to do on this page.

When someone gives the correct response, compliment him. Then read the instructions aloud. Allow the children to complete the page.

4. Using the pictures illustrating big and little, have the children cut out examples of large and small objects, or use construction paper to cut out circles, triangles, squares, and rectangles of different sizes and colors. Allow the children to glue them wherever they want on a large piece of paper. When they are finished, have them draw lines connecting matching items (big and little, same color, same shape). The matching lines do not need to be straight lines.

LESSON 7

MATERIALS NEEDED

- pencils
- red, yellow, green, blue, and brown crayons

Objectives:

1. To learn a new color, brown.

2. To identify shapes.

3. To identify big and little.

4. To match related objects one-to-one.

Teaching Pages 12, 13, and 14:

1. Give the children time to look at page 12. Ask what the picture is about, and ask what is missing in each one. After someone identifies the fishing line or the line that matches the two objects as missing, read the instructions aloud. When the children understand the instructions, have them draw lines to complete the matching.

2. Turn to page 13. Explain that on the last three pages the children have been matching two objects that go together—cowboy and cow, fisherman and fish. Point to the first box and ask: "In this box, which two objects go together?" (Dog and dish) Have the children draw a line to match each dog with a dish. Repeat the same procedure with the picture of plugs and outlets. Have the children identify the other pictures on the page and discuss how the objects are related. Allow the children to complete the page independently.

3. Read or recite John 3:16. Explain to the class that God wants each of us to let Jesus live in our hearts. He wants each of us to obey Him so we can live in heaven with Him forever. If we choose to obey Him, then we are matched one-to-one with God.

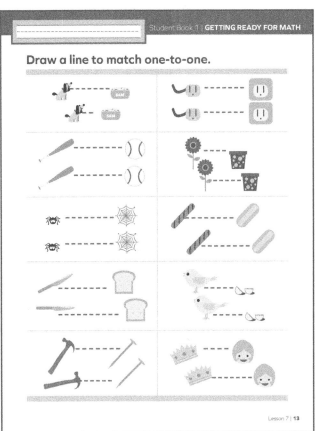

4. Turn to page 14. Have the children select the crayons for red, yellow, green, and blue. Select the brown crayon and tell the children that brown is a new color for them to learn. Ask the children to find the circles, squares, and rectangles on the page. Tell them to look at the whole page, and ask them what they can tell you about the pictures on the page. When they are able to tell you that they are big and little pictures, ask them to use their brown crayon to circle all of the little objects. Tell them to use any of the colors red, yellow, green, blue, or brown to color the circles, squares, and rectangles. Be sure the children can identify the colors as they are used and that they color in the lines and in the same direction.

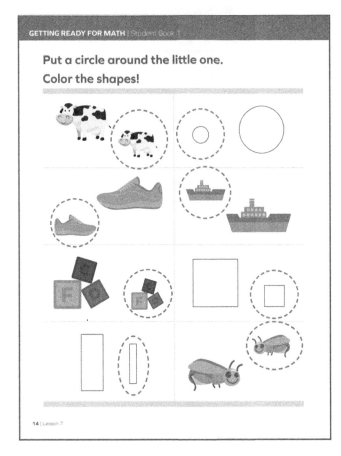

GETTING READY FOR MATH | Student Book 1

Put a circle around the little one.
Color the shapes!

14 | Lesson 7

LESSON 8

MATERIALS NEEDED

• pencils
• red, yellow, green, blue, and brown crayons

Objectives:

1. To recognize colors.

2. To identify big and little.

3. To match related objects one-to-one.

Teaching Pages 15 and 16:

1. Turn to page 15. Ask the children to identify and explain the relationship between each set of objects in each box. Ask them to find an illustration of an object colored red (apple), yellow (duck), green (caterpillar), blue (spoon), and brown (cow). Find other examples of these colors on the page. Read the directions for each section as the students complete the page.

2. Have the children turn to page 16.
   Use 1 Samuel 17:16–51 as a Bible reference. Let the children color the picture while listening to the story of David and Goliath. Remind them to add five stones for David. Add one stone to the sling. Have them tell who is big and who is little.
   Read to the children:
   David took his sling.
   He took 5 stones.
   Goliath laughed at David.
   David swung his sling.
   The stone hit Goliath.
   Down Goliath went.
   David thanked God.

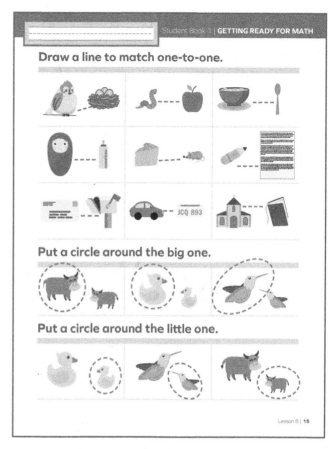

Student Book 1 | **GETTING READY FOR MATH**

Draw a line to match one-to-one.

Put a circle around the big one.

Put a circle around the little one.

Lesson 8 | 15

GETTING READY FOR MATH | Student Book 1

Color David and Goliath.

color this!

Teacher Check

Big

Little

16 | Lesson 8

LESSON 9

MATERIALS NEEDED

- pencils
- fifteen strips of colored paper (all one color) one inch by five inches in size, pasted or glued to cardboard or any objects that may be used for counting (beads, buttons, blocks)—one set for each student
- several sheets of plain paper
- red, yellow, blue, green, and brown crayons

Objectives:

1. To count to 5.

2. To match related objects.

Teaching Pages 17, 18 and 19:

1. Tape the strips of colored paper to a board in five groups—one strip in one group, two strips in another group, three strips in another, and so on.

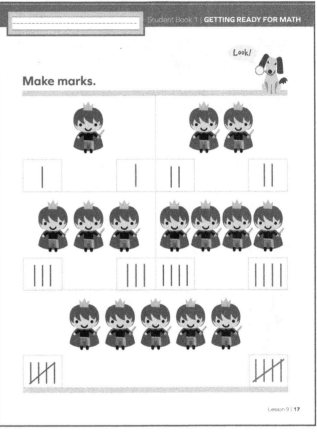

2. Explain to the students that these strips will be used for counting. Give the first strip to the students, and tell them that this represents one. Give the set of two strips to the students, and have them count 1-2. Give the set of three strips to the students, and have them count 1-2-3. Do the same with the sets of four and five. Do this several times until the students are familiar with handling and counting the strips. Start again with the first set of one strip, and tell the children to make one mark on a piece of paper to represent one strip. Then give them the set of two, and ask them to make two marks on the paper to represent the two strips. Have them count 1, 1-2 as they write down the marks. Continue with the sets of three, four, and five, writing the marks and counting aloud.

3. Turn to page 17 in the workbook. Point to the first box. Have the children place a finger on the boy, trace one mark, and count one. Point to the second box. Have the children point to one boy and trace one mark with their finger. Then point to the second boy and trace the second mark with their finger. Emphasize that there is one mark for each boy. Tell the children to count 1-2 as they trace the marks. Repeat this exercise with the remaining boxes. Draw the children's attention to the way the fifth mark is made when there is a total of five marks. Then have the children mark tally marks in each blank box.

4. Turn to page 18. Ask the children to look at the pictures in the boxes. Have them identify the objects in the pictures and discuss their relationship to each other. Talk about the colors on the page. Ask the children if they can remember how to match related items. Review pages 10, 11, and 12. Read the directions at the top of page 18, and have the children complete the page independently.

5. Turn to page 19. Ask: "Who are the people in the picture?" "How are the children dressed and why are they dressed as they are?" (They represent different countries.) Tell the children to draw a line from each child to the extended hand of Jesus. Read aloud: "We are all one in Christ. He is shepherd to all peoples and nations." Have the students use their crayons to color the picture. Read aloud John 3:16: "For God so loved the world, that he gave his only begotten Son, that whosoever believeth in him should not perish, but have everlasting life."

LESSON 10

MATERIALS NEEDED

- pencils
- fifteen strips of colored paper or any objects that may be used for counting

Objectives:

1. To count to 5.

2. To identify shapes.

Teaching Pages 20 and 21:

1. Use the colored strips as in Lesson 9 to have the students count to 1, 1-2, 1-2-3, 1-2-3-4, 1-2-3-4-5. Repeat the exercise several times.

2. Turn to page 20 in the workbook. Remind the children that the objects on this page are called shapes. Ask them if they can remember the names of the shapes. Ask: "Can you find a green square? a yellow triangle? a blue rectangle? a red circle?" Tell the children that you want them to count the shapes and make a mark for each one in the box. Have them count aloud as they make their marks: one circle; one rectangle; one triangle - two triangles - three triangles - four triangles; one circle - two circles - three circles; and so on until the page is completed.

3. Turn to page 21. Talk to the children about the pictures on the page. Have they seen some of these pictures before? Read the directions at the top of the page. Have the children count the pictures and make marks in each box. Have them count aloud as they make their marks.

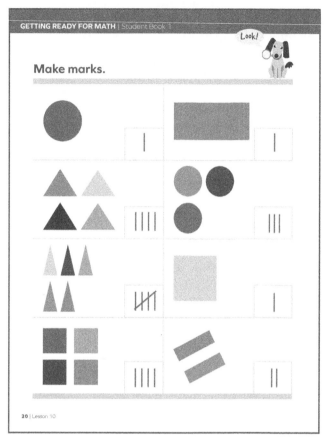

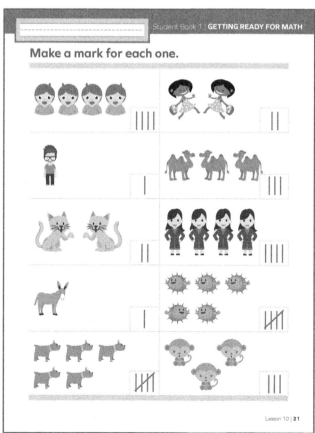

MATH KINDERGARTEN

Lessons 11–20

LESSON 11

MATERIALS NEEDED

- pencils
- red, yellow, blue, green, and brown crayons

Objectives:

1. To count to 5.

2. To identify shapes.

3. To match one-to-one.

4. To identify big and little.

Teaching Pages 22, 23, and 24:

1. Turn to page 22 in the workbook. Have the children identify the objects in the pictures. Have them count the objects while making a mark in the squares: one mitten - two mittens; one pot - two pots - three pots - four pots; and so on until the page is completed. Have the students follow the same instructions for page 23.

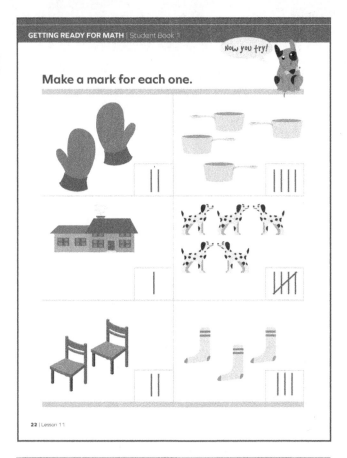

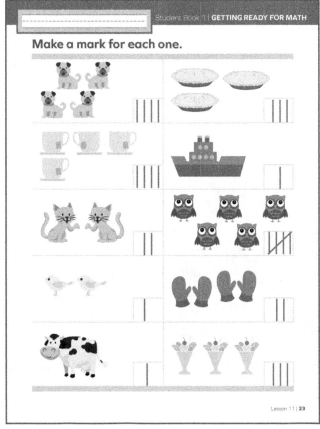

2. Turn to page 24. Read the instructions for the first section and have the students complete the section. Do the same for sections two and three. Try to give as little help as possible. Then, instruct the students this way: Use your *brown* crayon to circle the can of paint and the carrot. Use your *blue* crayon to circle the *red* squares. Use your *red* crayon to circle the *blue* rectangle. Use your *yellow* crayon to circle the *green* triangle. Use your *green* crayon to circle the *brown* circle. Do not hurry the children with this exercise. Make it similar to a hide and seek game.

LESSON 12

MATERIALS NEEDED

- pencils
- paper
- fifteen strips of colored paper or any objects that may be used for counting

Objectives:

1. To write the number symbols 1, 2, 3, 4, and 5.

Teaching Pages 25 and 26:

1. Explain to the children that they are ready to learn to write the number symbols. Turn to page 25 and read the title aloud. Point to the first row. Call attention to one chick, then to the one mark. Point to the number *1* and state that this is the number *1*. Point to the second row. Call attention to the two chicks and the two marks for the chicks. Then identify the number *2*. Continue this down the page. Have the students look at each number symbol and say its name several times.

2. Talk to the students about proper posture and how to hold the pencil before continuing to page 26. Students should sit up straight with legs under the table or desk. They should hold the pencil firmly and so that they can see their work.

Look!

Write numbers to 5.

	Mark	Number
	I	1
	II	2
	III	3
	IIII	4
	IIII	5

Lesson 12 | **25**

3. Turn to page 26. Have the students read the numbers on the page. Have the students trace the numbers on the work page with their fingers. Explain to them that on the numbers *4* and *5*, they will draw one line and then lift their pencils to draw the second line. When they have traced the numbers several times and seem to understand, they are ready to practice writing the numbers. Place the colored strips in front of the students. Ask the students to pick up one strip and make a mark for that strip on a sheet of paper. Then have them write the correct number symbol. Have them say the number as they write it. Set the colored strip aside and have the students pick up two colored strips. Have them make two marks and write the number symbol for *two*. Continue this process for *three*, *four*, and *five*.

LESSON 13

MATERIALS NEEDED

- pencils
- objects for counting
- red, yellow, green, blue, and brown crayons

Objectives:

1. To count from 1 to 5.

2. To write the number symbols 1, 2, 3, 4, and 5.

Teaching Pages 27 and 28:

1. Have the children review counting from one to five using their colored strips.

2. Turn to page 27 and read the number symbols with the students. Beginning with *one*, ask the students to show how many strips are represented by each number. Have the students trace the numbers with their fingers. Be sure that they have good posture and are holding their pencils correctly while they write the numbers. Complete page 28 in the same way.

3. Give the students a plain piece of paper (it may be colored paper) and pencil or crayon. Have them place their hand on the paper and draw around it. After completing the drawing, have them count the number of fingers including the thumb on the drawing. Tell them to write a number (1-2-3-4-5) on each one, and then let them color the drawing.

Student Book 1 | GETTING READY FOR MATH

Write!

Teacher Check

1
2
3
4
5

Lesson 13 | 27

GETTING READY FOR MATH | Student Book 1

Try it again!

Teacher Check

1 2 3 4 5

28 | Lesson 13

LESSON 14

MATERIALS NEEDED

- pencils
- paper
- objects for counting
- red, yellow, blue, green, and brown crayons

Objectives:

1. To count from 1 to 5.

2. To write the number symbols 1, 2, 3, 4, and 5.

3. To identify big and little, right and left, above and below, inside and outside.

Teaching Pages 29, 30, and 31:

1. Have the students review counting to five with the colored strips. In any order, give them a set of strips up to five and ask them to count "how many?" Ask them to write the number symbol on a sheet of paper as they identify the number in the set. Students who are having difficulty should write the marks first and then the symbols. They may use page 25 in their workbooks as a guide.

2. Turn to page 29. Read each set of directions aloud and have the students complete the page independently.

3. Turn to page 30. Follow these instructions: "Find the *two* circles on the page. Draw a line *below* the circle that is on the *right*." "Find the *two* hair brushes on the page. Draw a circle around the *big* brush that is above the *little* brush." "Find the *two* rectangles on the page. Draw a *yellow* line on *top* of the *big* rectangle." "Find the car *inside* a *little* garage. Circle the car." "Find the moon and stars *outside* a *big* house. Circle the moon and stars." "Find the *two* Holy Bibles on the page. Circle the Bible that is on the *left*." "Circle the *big* tree with a *green* crayon and the *little* pint of milk with a *blue* crayon." "Circle the paintbrush below the *little* tree."

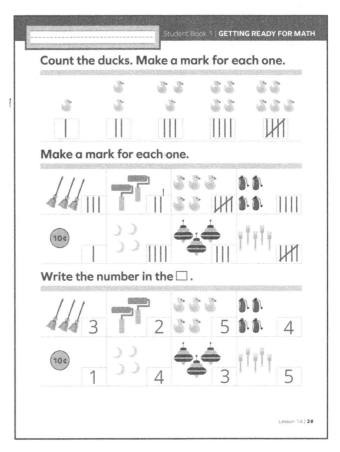

4. Introduce page 31 by reading or telling the story of Noah and God's instructions to him about taking the animals and his family into the ark. (Genesis 6:9–22) Emphasize the number of sons and the number of each kind of animal. Ask the children if they think Noah made a mark for each elephant, giraffe, tiger, and so on that went into the ark. Have the children count and then write the correct symbol in each box. Let them color the page using the colors they have learned.

LESSON 15

MATERIALS NEEDED

- pencils
- paper
- red, yellow, blue, green, and brown crayons

Objectives:

1. To write the number symbols 1, 2, 3, 4, and 5.

2. To identify right and left, big and little, above and below.

3. To match one-to-one.

4. To identify shapes.

Teaching Pages 32, 33, and 34:

1. Draw some circles, squares, rectangles, and triangles on a piece of paper and review their names with the students. Turn to page 32 in the workbook. Select different shapes on the page and instruct the students to "Circle the *large* green rectangle," "Circle the *small* red square," "Underline the *large* yellow circle." Continue doing this until you have included all shapes on the page.

2. Turn to page 33. Go over each picture so that the children are familiar with the items. Ask them how many items are in each picture. Ask if any of the pictures are alike (five are objects, three are shapes). Instruct the children to "Color the circle on the *right* green, and the circle on the *left* yellow," "Color the *big* triangle red and the *little* triangle brown," "Use the blue crayon to color the rectangle that is *above*, and the red crayon to color the rectangle that is *below*." Have the students complete the page by drawing a circle around the little one.

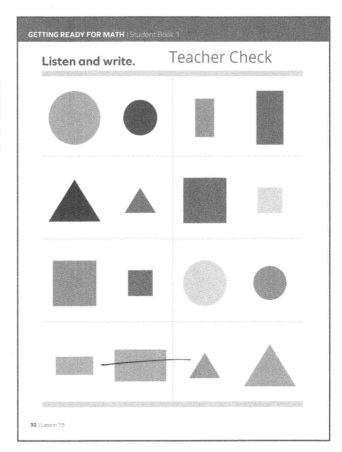

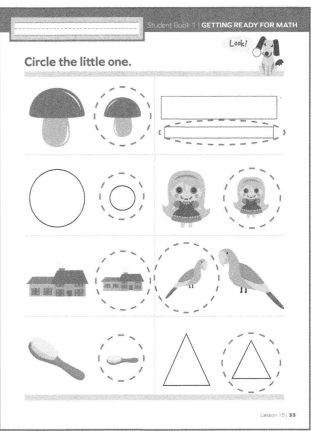

3. Turn to page 34. Read the instructions for the first exercise and allow the students to complete it independently. Read the second set of instructions and allow the students to complete that exercise. Do the same with the third and fourth sections on the page.

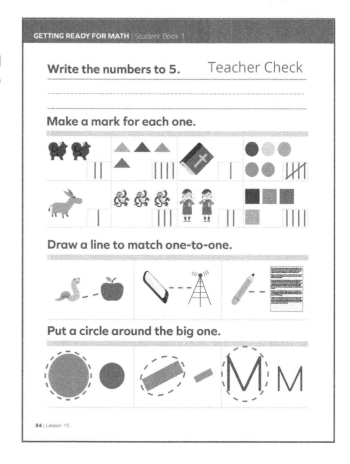

LESSON 16

MATERIALS NEEDED

- pencils
- paper
- objects for counting

Objectives:

1. To use the number symbols to count to 3.

2. To write the number symbols 1 to 5.

Teaching Pages 35, 36, and 37:

1. Place six strips in front of each student in groups of one, two, and three. Ask the children to count how many and then make a mark on a sheet of paper for each strip in each group.

2. Turn to page 35. Tell the children that the ducks are like their marks. Point to the title of the page and read aloud. Have the children look at the first row on the page and point to the duck. State that there is one mark for the one duck. Point to the number *1*. Have the children say *one* aloud. Do the same with the next rows pointing out the numbers *2* and *3*. Practice counting aloud: *one; one, two; one two, three*.

3. Turn to page 36. Read the instructions at the top of the page. Have the children point to the first box and make a mark for each object in the box. Have the children count the objects aloud. Complete the first section. Read the instructions in the middle of the page. Have the children count the objects aloud and write the number in the box.

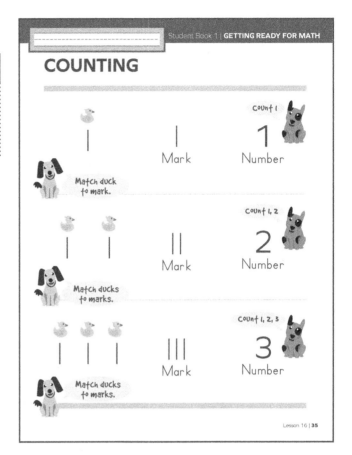

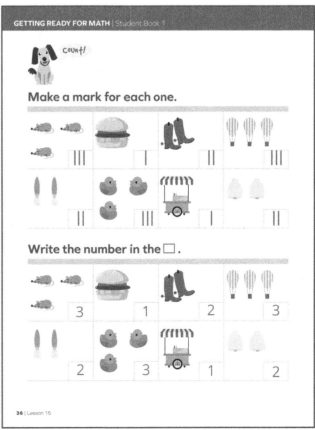

4. Turn to page 37 and read the instructions. Review proper posture and how to hold the pencil with the children.

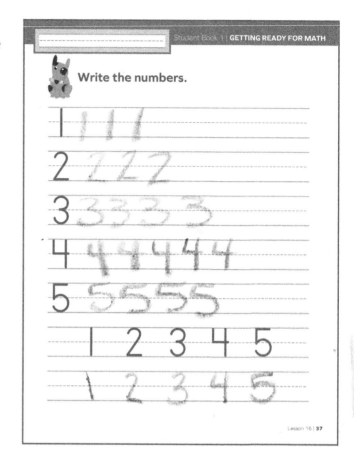

LESSON 17

MATERIALS NEEDED

- pencils
- paper
- objects for counting

Objectives:

1. To use the number symbols to count to 5.

2. To write the number symbols 1 to 5.

Teaching Pages 38, 39, and 40:

1. Place fifteen strips in groups of one, two, three, four, and five in front of each student. Ask the children to count how many and then make a mark on a sheet of paper for each strip in each group.

2. Turn to page 38. Tell the children that the ducks are like their marks. Have the children look at the first row on the page and point to the ducks. State that there is one mark for each duck. Point to the number *4*. Have the children say *four* aloud. Do the same with the next row pointing out the number *5*. Practice counting aloud: *one, two, three, four; one, two, three, four, five*.

3. Turn to page 39. Read the instructions at the top of the page aloud. Have the children point to the first box and make a mark for each object in the box. Have the children count the objects aloud and count the marks aloud. Complete the first section. Read the instructions in the middle of the page aloud. Have the children count the objects aloud and write the number in the box.

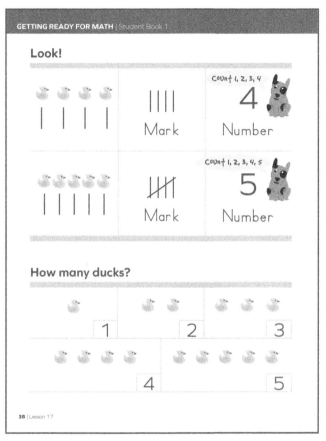

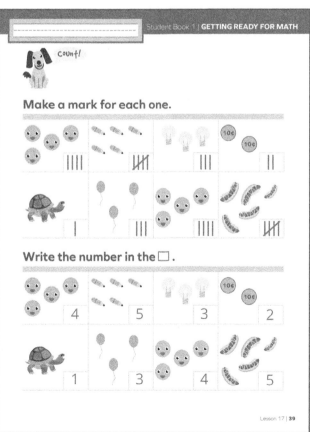

4. Turn to page 40. Read the instructions at the top of the page aloud. Be sure the children understand that they are to write the number. Children who are having difficulty should point to each object and count it aloud. They may refer to page 25, if necessary.

LESSON 18

MATERIALS NEEDED

• pencils

Objectives:

1. To recognize big and little.

2. To match one-to-one.

3. To make a mark for each object.

4. To write numbers 1 to 5.

Teaching Pages 41 and 42:

1. Turn to pages 41 and 42. Point to each set of instructions. Read one set of instructions, have the children complete that section, and then read the next set of instructions until the two pages are completed.

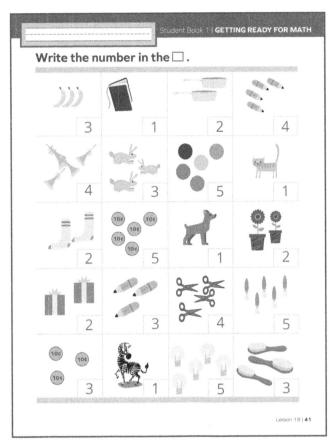

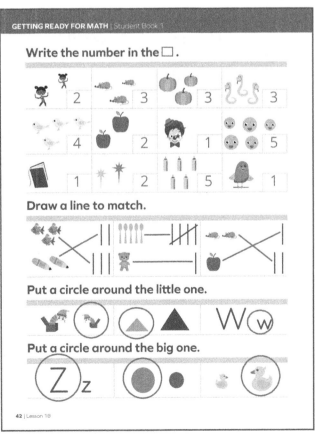

LESSON 19

MATERIALS NEEDED

- pencils
- red, yellow, green, blue, and brown crayons

Objectives:

1. To write numbers 1 to 5.

2. To learn ordinal (order) numbers.

Teaching Page 43:

1. Turn to page 43. Ask the children to read the numbers at the top of the page. Introduce the words *I have* to them and ask them to repeat the words as they go down the page. Tell them that they are to write a number on the line to make the sentence true. The students may read the first words *I have* and the final word(s) should be read to them. When they have completed this exercise, show them the balloons at the bottom of the page.

2. Introduce the words *first*, *second*, *third*, *fourth*, and *fifth* to them. Explain that these words tell us the order that things are in. Have them say the words aloud. Talk to them about the relationship between one and first, two and second, three and third, four and fourth, five and fifth. Have them count the balloons at the bottom of the page *1-2-3-4-5*. Then say to them as you point to the balloon "This is the first balloon, this is the second balloon, this is the third balloon, this is the fourth balloon, and this is the fifth balloon." Ask them to color the first balloon yellow, the second balloon green, the third balloon brown, the fourth balloon red, and the fifth balloon blue.

LESSON 20

MATERIALS NEEDED

• pencils
• brown, yellow, blue, and green crayons

Objectives:

1. To recognize big and little.

2. To match one-to-one.

3. To recognize colors and shapes.

4. To make a mark for each object.

5. To write numbers 1 to 5.

Teaching Pages 44 and 45:

1. Turn to pages 44 and 45. Point to each set of instructions. Read one set of instructions, and allow the children to complete that section. Then read the next set of instructions. The last exercise is for recognition of both colors and shapes. Give the students the opportunity to select the correct color and the correct shape as the directions are read to them. Color the *triangles* green, the *circles* yellow, the *rectangles* blue, and the *square(s)* brown.

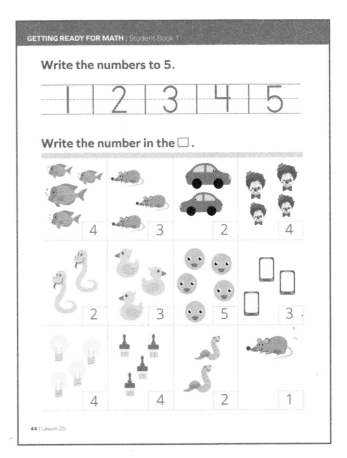

MATH KINDERGARTEN

Lessons 21–30

LESSON 21

MATERIALS NEEDED

- pencils
- red, yellow, blue, and green crayons

Objectives:

1. To recognize big and little.

2. To match one-to-one.

3. To recognize colors and shapes.

4. To make a mark for each object.

5. To write numbers 1 to 5.

Teaching Pages 46 and 47:

1. Turn to pages 46 and 47. Point to each set of instructions. Read one set of instructions and allow the children to complete that section. Then read the next set of instructions. The last exercise is for recognition of both colors and shapes. Give the students the opportunity to select the correct color and the correct shape as the directions are read to them. Color the *circle(s) blue,* the *squares* red, the *triangles* green, and the *rectangles* yellow.

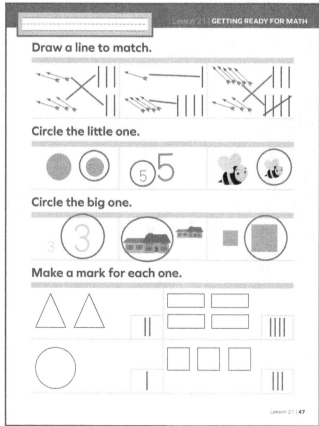

LESSON 22

MATERIALS NEEDED

- pencils
- fifteen objects for counting (colored strips, beads, pencils, erasers, blocks, utensils, etc.)

Objectives:

1. To estimate objects to make a set of 5.

2. To count the number of objects in a set.

3. To write the correct number for a set.

Teaching Pages 48 and 49:

1. Turn to page 48. Read the title of the page with the students. Explain to the students that a set is any group of objects or things. Call attention to the first set and ask the children to describe it (a set of houses). State that since there is one object in this set, *1* is the number for the set. Continue this discussion for each set on the page. Have the students write the numbers *1* through *5* next to each of the printed numbers. Be sure they use the correct method in forming their numbers.

2. Turn to page 49. Explain to the students that any objects grouped together may become a set. Help them identify the objects on the page. Read the directions aloud. Do the first two or three sets together. Have the children complete the page independently.

3. Place *fourteen* objects in front of each of the students. Ask them if they think there are enough objects to make sets of *1, 2, 3, 4,* and *5* objects (yes or no). Do not expect the children to be able to count to *fourteen*. This is an exercise in estimation. Ask them what they will need to do to prove their answer. Explain what the word *prove* means and how important it is in math. If they do not understand what is expected of them, ask them questions until they are ready to

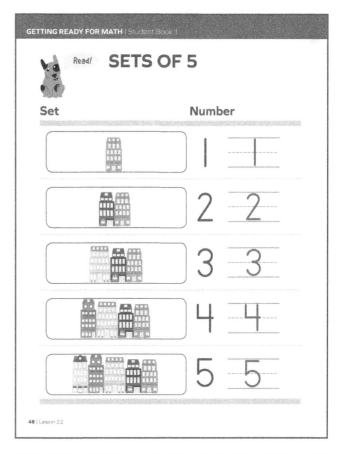

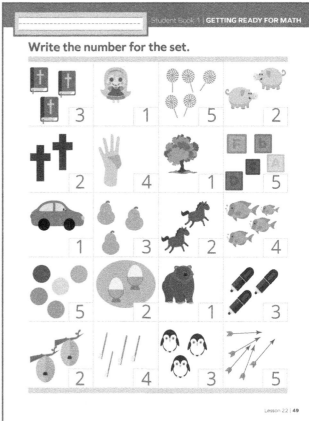

100%

group the objects into sets of *1, 2, 3, 4,* and *5.* When the students realize they lack one object to complete the sets, give them the last object and congratulate them for doing so well. It does not matter what order they use to complete the sets.

LESSON 23

MATERIALS NEEDED

- pencils
- paper
- colored construction paper
- paste or glue
- scissors
- red, yellow, blue, green, brown, and purple crayons

Objectives:

1. To count the number of objects in a set of 5.

2. To write the correct number for a set.

3. To identify shapes.

4. To learn the color purple.

Teaching Pages 50 and 51:

1. Place the crayons in front of the children, and ask them which one is new to them (purple). Tell them the name of the new color and that they will be using that color today.

2. Turn to pages 50 and 51. Read the title and the directions aloud. Have the children use paper and scissors to cut out groups of squares, triangles, rectangles, and circles using the construction paper. They may decorate them using their crayons including the new color, purple. When they have enough shapes cut out, have them paste the shapes in the ovals on the page to complete the different sets. If the students have difficulty in making their objects small enough, allow them to paste the shapes in sets on a separate piece of paper.

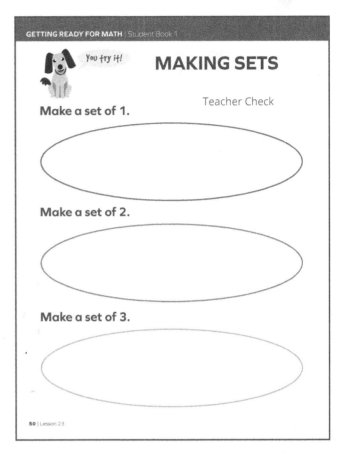

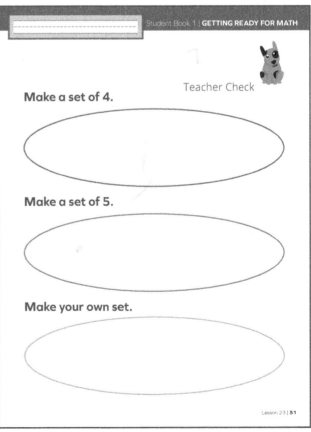

LESSON 24

MATERIALS NEEDED

- pencils
- red, yellow, blue, green, brown, and purple crayons

Objectives:

1. To count the number of objects in a set of 5.

2. To write the correct number for a set.

3. To identify the color purple.

Teaching Pages 52, 53, 54:

1. Turn to page 52. Read the instructions for the first exercise on the page. Have the children complete the exercise with as little help as possible. Read the directions for the second exercise on the page, and have the students complete it independently.

2. Turn to page 53. Ask the students how they would identify the objects on this page. (They are grouped in sets.) Ask them to write the number in each set on the line. Tell them to use their purple crayon to finish coloring each picture. Emphasize that they color inside the lines and in one direction. Ask them which direction they are going to color each object before beginning. This will help them to think ahead and develop neat habits.

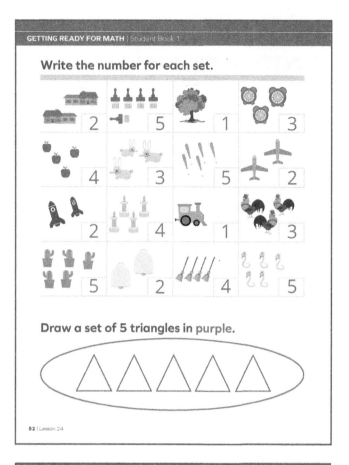

3. Turn to page 54. Read the Bible verses for each set. The children should listen for the name and number of objects. (Remind the children of the picture they colored in Lesson 8.) Have them write the number in the sets on the line. They may illustrate the verses using the colors they have learned.

LESSON 25

MATERIALS NEEDED

- pencils
- forty-five objects for counting—one set for each student
- several sheets of plain paper

Objectives:

1. To use strips and tally marks to count to 9.

2. To identify things that are alike.

Teaching Pages 55, 56, and 57:

1. Using the objects for counting and a piece of paper, review counting with tally marks *1* to *5*. Explain to the children that they are going to learn to count to *9* by using tally marks. Have the students make one set each of *1, 2, 3, 4,* and *5* objects. Set these aside but close enough so that the students can still refer to them. Place a set of *six* objects in front of each student. Have the students make tally marks on a piece of paper for each object in the set. Have them count to *six* as they make the marks. Use the same method to count to *seven, eight,* and *nine.* Go over the sets again so that the students become familiar with counting to *nine.*

2. Turn to page 55 and identify the objects on the page. Have the students count aloud as they trace the tally marks with their fingers.

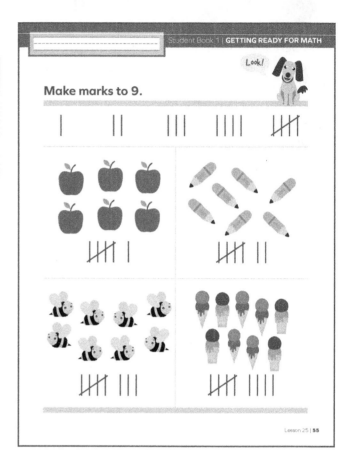

Make marks to 9.

3. Turn to pages 56 and 57. Go over the pictures on the pages. Ask questions about what pictures are similar, alike, or have something in common. (eating: sodas, carrots, toast, pie, bananas) (transportation: cars, planes, rockets) Ask them to pick three or four objects and tell a story about the objects. (For example: the lips, the toast, and the mirror.) Read the directions at the top of each page and have the children complete the pages.

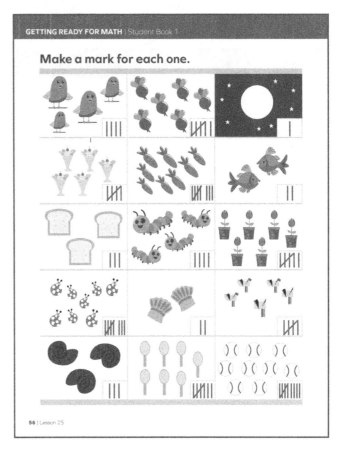

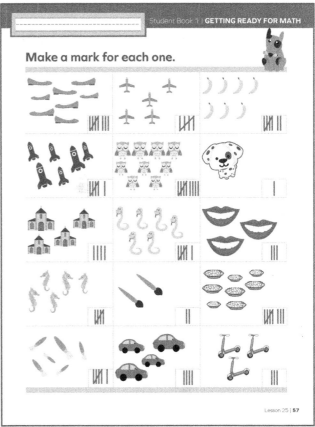

LESSON 26

MATERIALS NEEDED

- pencils
- samples of big and little objects
- red, yellow, blue, green, brown, and purple crayons

Objectives:

1. To write numbers 1 to 5.

2. To match one-to-one.

3. To identify big and little objects.

Teaching Pages 58 and 59:

1. Turn to page 58. Review the instructions for Lesson 12 about proper posture and holding the pencil. Tell the students to trace over each number. Have them write the numbers.

2. Turn to page 59. Review big and little by using the sample objects. Review matching one-to-one by drawing a line. Work with the students by identifying the first object on the page. Then select a certain color for them to use to draw a line to the matching object. Continue doing this until the page is complete and all six colors have been used.

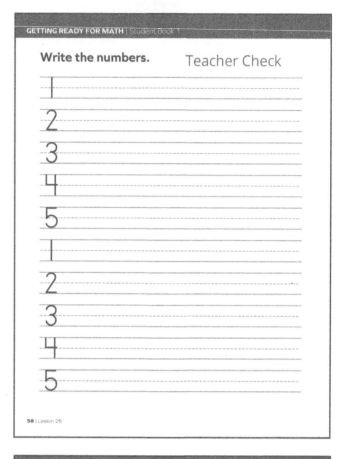

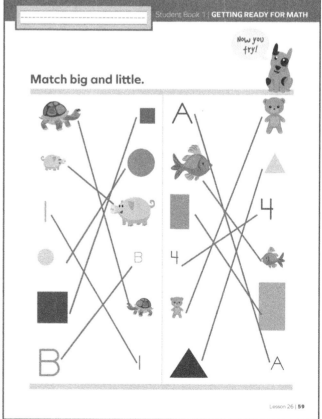

LESSON 27

MATERIALS NEEDED

- pencils
- a group of big and little objects
- 9 similar objects (blocks, beans, toothpicks)

Objectives:

1. To recognize order in big and little.

2. To learn ordinal (order) numbers to ninth.

3. To count to 9 using tally marks.

4. To write numbers 1 to 5.

Teaching Page 60:

1. Tell the children that we have another way of talking about numbers. Sometimes numbers will tell us about order. Take a group of the big and little objects and arrange them in order of smallest to largest. Talk to the students about what order means and what order these objects are in (little to big). Mix the objects and then ask the students to arrange the objects from big to little. Place *nine* similar objects in front of the students and have them count from *one* to *nine*. Then pick up the *first* object and say, "This is the first object." Continue doing this through the *nine* objects. Discuss the similarity of *one* and *first, two* and *second, three* and *third, four* and *fourth, five* and *fifth, six* and *sixth, seven* and *seventh, eight* and *eighth, nine* and *ninth*. Ask the students to say the order numbers with you.

2. Turn to page 60. Read the directions at the top of the page. Have the students make tally marks for each object. Read the directions for the second exercise. Have the students write the number for these objects. Point to the balls at the top of the page. Read with the students as they count: *1-2-3-4-5-6-7-8-9*. Then have them say aloud: *first, second, third, fourth, fifth, sixth, seventh, eighth, ninth*.

LESSON 28

MATERIALS NEEDED

• pencils

Objectives:

1. To count to 9 using tally marks.

2. To write numbers 1 to 9.

Teaching Pages 61, 62, and 63:

1. Turn to page 61. Have the children point to the first row of numbers (1 to 5), and ask them to read these numbers aloud as they point to each one. Point to the number *3*. Ask: "What number is this?" "How many marks are there?" "How many crayons are there?" Repeat with the other numerals *1* to *5* in random order. Point to the second row. Have the children use their fingers to show that one mark is used for each crayon. Then point to the number *6* and state that this symbol is the number *6*. Repeat the procedure with numbers *7*, *8*, *9*. Have the children trace the numbers at the bottom of the page with their fingers and say the numbers aloud.

2. Turn to page 62. Be sure the students have proper posture and are holding their pencils correctly. Have them write each number four times and then repeat the process.

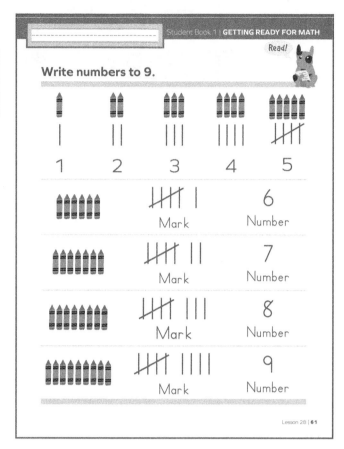

3. Turn to page 63. Be sure the students have proper posture and are holding their pencils correctly. Have them write each number four times.

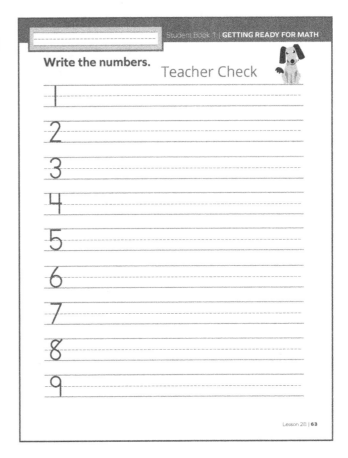

LESSON 29

MATERIALS NEEDED

- pencils
- red, yellow, green, blue, brown, and purple crayons

Objectives:

1. To write numbers 1 to 9.

2. To identify sets from 1 to 9.

3. To use colors through purple.

Teaching Pages 64, 65, and 66:

1. Turn to page 64. Read the directions at the top of the page. Allow the children to refer back to page 62, if necessary. Be sure that they are following correct procedures to write the numbers.

2. Turn to page 65. Read the directions on the page. Try to have the students complete this page as independently as possible.

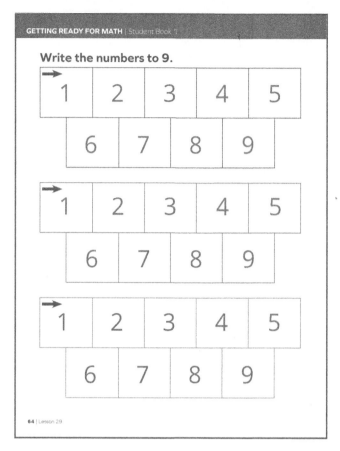

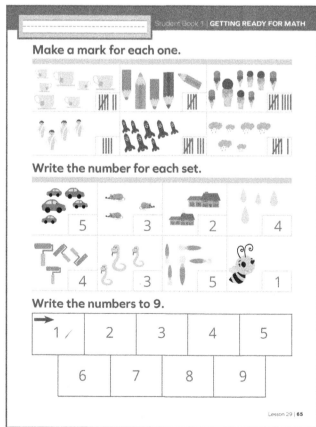

3. Turn to page 66. Tell the class that they have been learning to write the number symbols *1* to *9*. Say that God is aware of their efforts. He likes us to learn and do our very best. Say God is glad we can write numbers. Tell the students there is something even more important God wants us to learn to write, and we do not use paper or pencils. Read Proverbs 7:1–3. Discuss the question at the bottom of the worksheet. Allow the children time to complete their coloring. Remind them to color in the lines and in the same direction.

Listen to the Bible verses. Color.

Teacher Check   Proverbs 7:1-3

What does it mean to write God's words on your heart?

66 | Lesson 29

LESSON 30

MATERIALS NEEDED

• pencils
• eighteen pieces of cardboard cut two inches by three inches—write the number 1 on two pieces, the number 2 on two pieces, the number 3 on two pieces, and so on through 9 (keep these sets for future use)

Objectives:

1. To use marks to count to 6.

2. To write the numbers to 6.

3. To learn to match numbers through 9.

Teaching Pages 67 and 68:

1. Turn to page 67. Point to the title and read it aloud. Look at each set of ducks one at a time. Count the number of ducks, pointing to each one in the set. Then read with the students the numbers beneath that particular set. Call attention to the ducks at the bottom of the page. Show that each duck is matched to a mark. Emphasize that the number of tally marks is the same as the number of ducks. Point to the number 6. Have the class count to 6. Then count the ducks.

2. Turn to page 68. Point to each set of directions as you read them. Make sure the children understand what they are to do. Allow the children to complete the page independently.

3. Tell the children to mix the eighteen pieces of cardboard with the numbers written on them and turn them face down in front of them (three rows with six cards to a row). Tell them you are going to play a game of concentration. Let the students take the first turn by picking up any two cards, trying to match two cards with the same number symbol. If they cannot, the two cards are put face down in the same position from which they were picked up, and the next

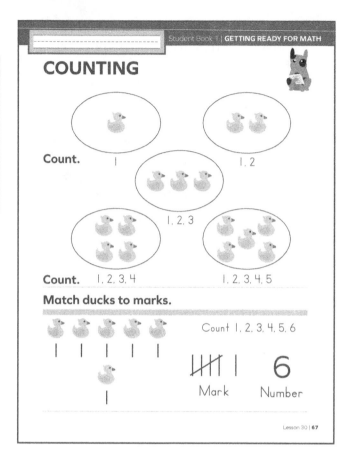

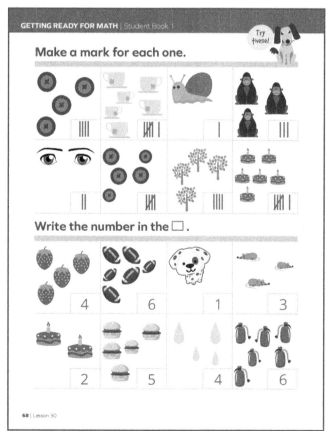

person takes a turn. The person who makes the most matches wins the game. Play the game several times. Be sure to say the names of the numbers as they are matched. (For students having difficulty, try with just the numbers 1 through 5.)

— Counted Alone

MATH KINDERGARTEN

Lessons 31–40

LESSON 31

MATERIALS NEEDED

- pencils
- nine pieces of cardboard cut two inches by three inches, numbered 1 through 9

Objectives:

1. To use marks to count to 9.

2. To write the numbers 1 through 9.

Teaching Pages 69, 70, and 71:

1. Turn to page 69. Read the directions at the top of the page. Show that each duck is matched to a mark. Point to the tally marks in the middle of the row. Say that the number of tally marks is the same as the number of ducks. Point to the number 7. Have the children count to 7. Count the ducks. Count the tally marks. Repeat this procedure with the next two rows.

2. Turn to page 70. Read the directions at the top of the page to the students. Have them complete the exercise. Do the same with the directions at the middle of the page.

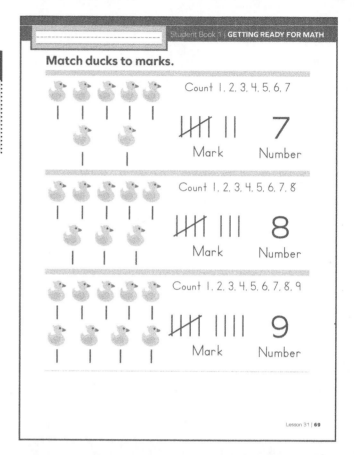

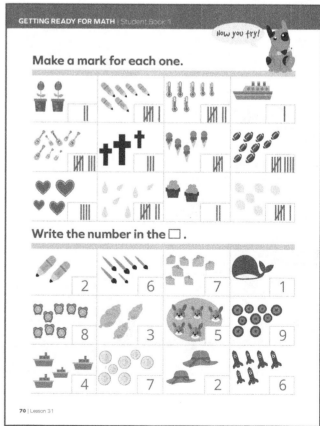

3. Turn to page 71. Read the directions at the top of the page to the students. Have them complete the exercise. Let them refer to page 63 to be sure they are forming their numbers correctly.

4. Use one set of cards (1 through 9). Have one student hold a card up in any order and have the other students count to that number. Use this procedure as a drill to practice counting.

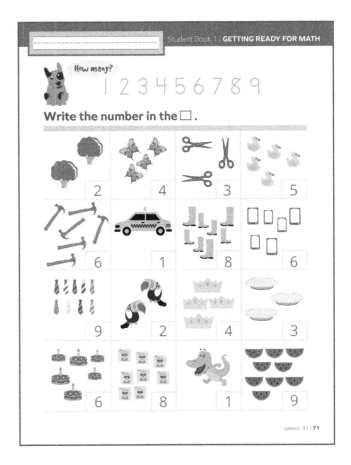

LESSON 32

MATERIALS NEEDED

- pencils
- one set of number cards from Lesson 30
- nine pieces of blank cardboard, two inches by three inches (keep these sets for future use)
- paste or glue

Objectives:

1. To use marks to count to 9.

2. To write the numbers 1 through 9.

3. To use ordinal (order) numbers.

4. To match objects and numbers.

Teaching Pages 72 and 73:

1. Complete these pages by doing page 73 first and page 72 second.

2. Turn to page 73. Have the children count the ducks and write the numbers. Ask them if they can say the order of the ducks. Review *first*, *second*, *third* and so on through *ninth* with them. Then, point to the *third* duck and say, "Which one is this?" (third duck) Ask the same question about several other ducks. Read the directions on the remainder of the page and have the students work independently.

3. Turn to page 72. Ask the students to identify and count aloud the objects in each picture. Have them cut out the pictures by cutting along the lines. Paste or glue the pictures on the nine pieces of blank cardboard. Take nine of the cards that have numbers written on them (1–9) from Lesson 30, and mix them with the cards the students have just made. Play a new game of concentration matching pictures and numbers.

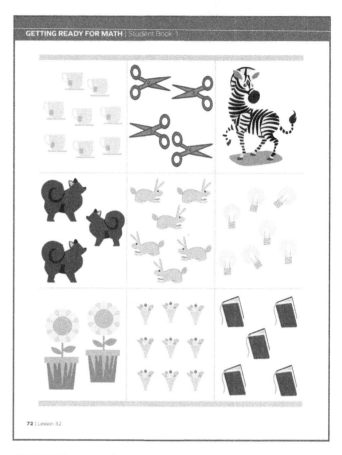

LESSON 33

MATERIALS NEEDED

• pencils
• forty-five objects for counting
• one set of cards marked 1 through 9

Objectives:

1. To use marks to count to 9.

2. To match objects and numbers.

3. To learn numbers before and after.

Teaching Pages 74 and 75:

1. Place a card with the number showing (any number 1 through 9) in front of the children, and ask them to pull the same number of objects from the group of eighteen objects. Do this in random order until you have used all nine cards.

2. Turn to page 74. Read the directions. Have the students match the objects with the numbers.

3. Place eighteen objects so that the children can reach them. Place five objects directly in front of the children. Ask them to select the number of objects for the set before the set of five (four) and after the set of five (six). Do this with several sets of objects *1* through *9* in any order. Place the cards in number order *1* through *9*, and put them in reach of the children. Place the number card *6* in front of the students, and ask them to select the number card *before* and the number card *after*. Do this with all of the numbers *2* through *8*. The students may use oral counting and the numbers on page 75 if they are having difficulty.

4. Turn to page 75. Have the students read the number symbols at the top of the page orally. Read the directions at the top of the page, and tell the students to write the numbers. Read the directions in the middle of the page, and tell the students to write those numbers.

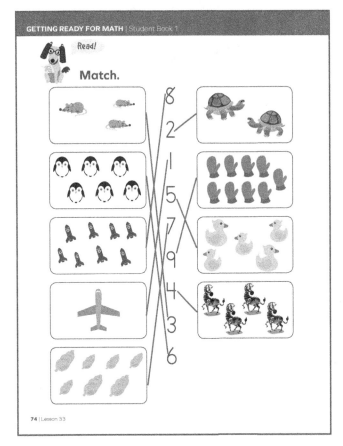

LESSON 34

MATERIALS NEEDED

• pencils

Objectives:

1. To review colors through purple.

2. To review directions—right, left, top, bottom.

3. To recognize sets to 9.

4. To write the numbers 1 through 9.

Teaching Pages 76 and 77:

1. Turn to pages 76 and 77. Ask the children how many objects shown on page 76 are also shown on page 77. Ask them if they are the same color. Help them identify the colors (ducks are yellow and raindrops are blue). Talk to them about the location (racquets are on the left side of page 76 and on the right side of page 77). Ask if the crowns are at the top, middle, or bottom of the pages. Ask them what picture on the page goes with the clouds? (rain) Who on the page would like to have it rain? (ducks, flowers, mushrooms) If it rained too hard, what would be used to wipe up? (mops) Have the children complete the page by writing the number for each set. Ask the children to compare the numbers of similar sets on page 76 to the numbers in the sets on page 77. Are they alike? Are they different?

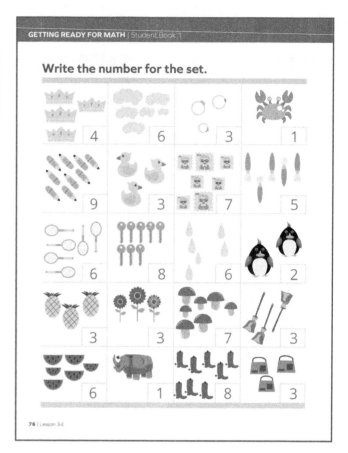

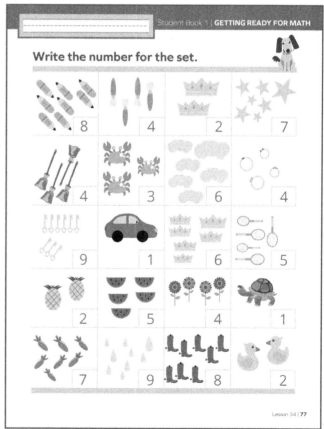

LESSON 35

MATERIALS NEEDED

- pencils
- paper bag
- twenty small objects (beans, beads)
- red, yellow, green, blue, brown, and purple crayons

Objectives:

1. To learn to estimate objects to 9.

2. To write the numbers for 1 to 9.

3. To use the colors through purple.

Teaching Pages 78, 79, and 80:

1. Turn to page 78. Have the students trace the numbers and then write each one four times. Be sure they use good penmanship.

2. Turn to page 79. Put a group of twenty objects in a bag and shake well. Tell the students to read the number (3) in the first column on the page. Ask the children to close their eyes and try to draw that many objects out of the bag. Tell them to put the objects down in front of them and make a tally mark in the second column for each object they have drawn out. Tell them to write the number symbol in the third column. Then ask them if the number of objects they drew out is the same as, bigger than, or smaller than the number *3*. Continue in the same manner with the rest of the numbers on the page.

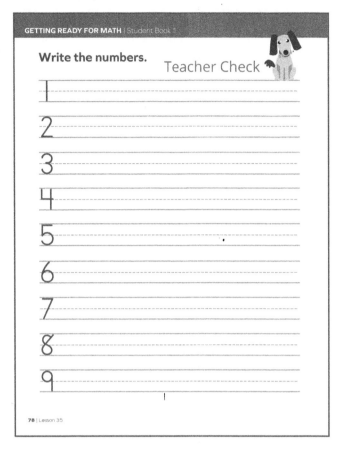

3. Turn to page 80. Read the directions to the children and have them complete the picture by drawing dot-to-dot. Ask them to describe the objects in the drawing. Ask them to identify the colors of each one of their crayons. Have them use their crayons to complete the drawing.

LESSON 36

MATERIALS NEEDED

- pencils
- thirty objects a size that the student may handle easily (pencil, eraser, block, utensil, etc.)
- colored paper
- red, yellow, green, blue, brown, and purple crayons
- scissors
- paste or glue

Objectives:

1. To identify a set.

2. To estimate objects to make a set.

3. To identify colors and shapes.

Teaching Pages 81, 82, and 83:

1. Review the definition of a set (a group). Place twenty-seven objects in front of the students. Ask them if they think there are enough objects for them to make sets of *6, 7, 8,* and *9* objects. Do not expect them to be able to count to thirty. This is an exercise in estimation. Ask them what they will need to do to prove their answer. Review what the word *prove* means. If the students do not understand what is expected of them, ask them questions until they are ready to group the objects into sets of *6, 7, 8,* and *9*. When the students realize they lack three objects to complete the sets, give them the three objects and congratulate them for doing so well. It does not matter what order they use to complete the sets.

2. Turn to pages 81, 82, and 83 in the workbooks. Have the students draw shapes of squares, rectangles, circles, and triangles on the colored paper. They should use different sizes and colors. Ask the students to identify colors and shapes as they make them. Then have the students cut out the shapes. Use the shapes, glue, and crayons

yes →

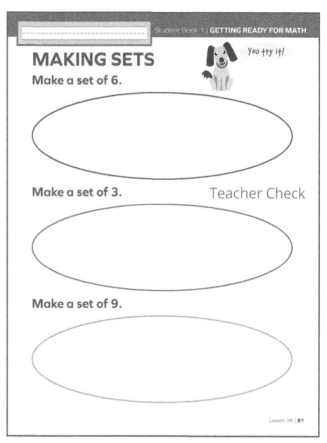

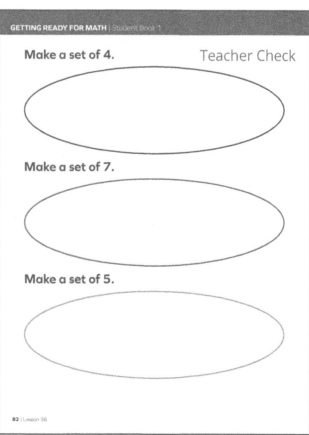

to complete the sets. The children may combine coloring and cutouts to make up their sets.

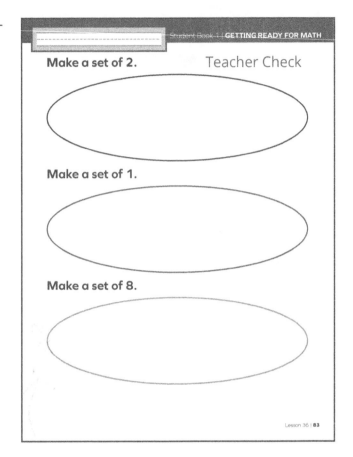

LESSON 37

MATERIALS NEEDED

- pencils
- red, yellow, green, blue, brown, and purple crayons

Objectives:

1. To count the number of objects in a set to 9.

2. To write the correct number for a set.

3. To identify colors and shapes.

4. To write the number before and after.

Teaching Pages 84 and 85:

1. Turn to pages 84 and 85. Read the first set of directions aloud. Allow the students to complete each exercise before reading the next directions. The students should complete these pages as independently as possible.

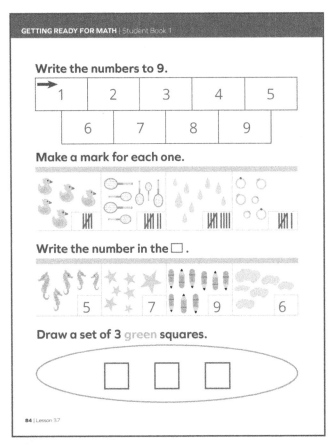

LESSON 38

MATERIALS NEEDED

• pencils

Objectives:

1. To identify big and little.

2. To write numbers and letters in order.

3. To write the numbers and letters before and after.

Teaching Pages 86 and 87:

1. Turn to page 86, and read the directions to the students. Have them read the numbers and the letters and then circle each big one. Read the directions at the bottom of the page. Have them complete the page by writing the numbers in order (1, 2, 3, 4) and the letters in order (A, B, C, D).

2. Turn to page 87, and read the directions to the students. Have them read the numbers and the letters and then circle each little one. Read the directions at the bottom of the page. Have them complete the page by writing the numbers or letters that are before and after. Use page 75 as a reference for number order, if necessary.

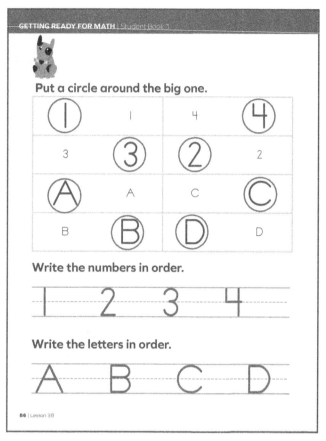

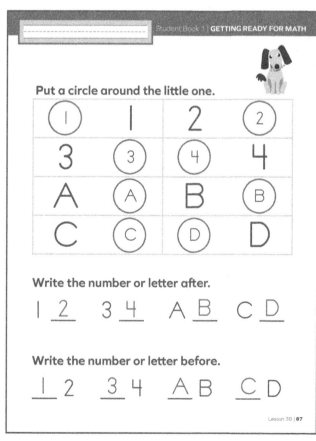

LESSON 39

MATERIALS NEEDED

- pencils
- red, yellow, green, blue, brown, and purple crayons

Objectives:

1. To write numbers to 9 in order.

2. To count using ordinal numbers and tally marks.

3. To write the numbers before and after.

4. To illustrate using shapes and colors.

Teaching Pages 88, 89, and 90:

1. Turn to pages 88, 89, and 90. These pages will test the students' ability to follow directions. Read a set of directions and have the children complete the exercise. Be sure the children understand the directions. For example, in the second exercise they should make marks, not write a number. If they start to do an exercise incorrectly, let them do a few, then stop them and read the directions again. Tell them it is important to listen and follow directions carefully. In the first exercise, the students are asked to write the numbers to 9. When they have completed this exercise, ask them to put their fingers on the first box and say aloud, "This is the ___ box" (first), "This is the ___ box" (second), "This is the ___ box" (third), and continue through the ninth box. This is an oral exercise and it may require some help from the teacher. Complete the remainder of pages 88, 89, and 90.

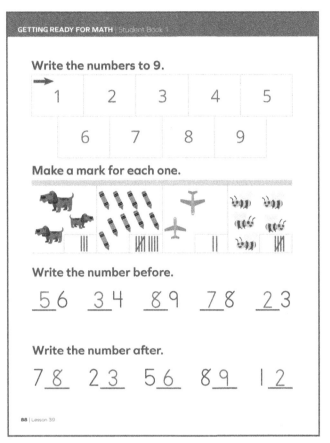

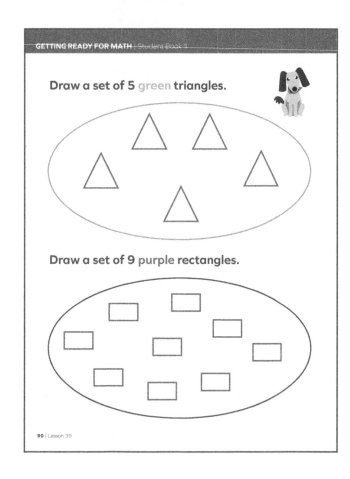

LESSON 40

MATERIALS NEEDED

- pencils
- red, yellow, green, blue, brown, and purple crayons

Objectives:

1. To write numbers to 9 in order.

2. To count using ordinal numbers and tally marks.

3. To write the numbers before and after.

4. To illustrate using shapes and colors.

Teaching Pages 91, 92, and 93:

1. Turn to pages 91, 92, and 93. Pages 91, 92, and 93 are very similar to pages 88, 89, and 90. They will allow the teacher and students another opportunity to review the skills covered on those pages. Read the set of directions and have the children complete the exercise. In the first exercise, the students are asked to write the numbers to 9. When they have completed this exercise, ask them to put their fingers on the first box and say aloud, "This is the ____ box" (first), "This is the ____ box" (second), "This is the ____ box" (third), and continue through the ninth box. Complete the remainder of pages 91, 92, and 93.

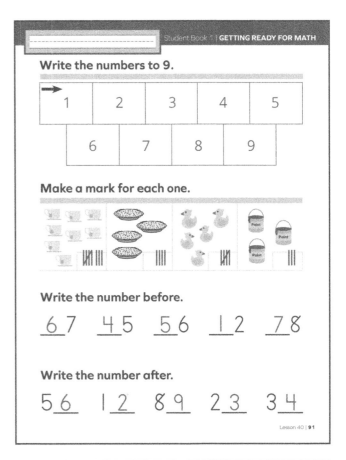

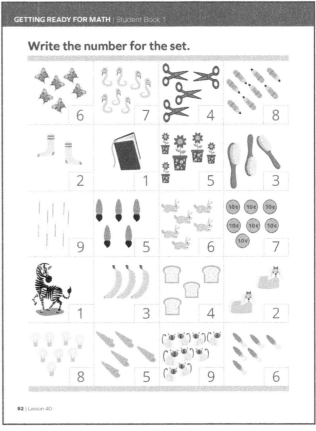

Draw a set of 6 yellow squares.

Draw a set of 8 blue circles.

Lesson 40 | **93**

MATH KINDERGARTEN

Lessons 41–50

LESSON 41

MATERIALS NEEDED

- pencils
- objects for counting (colored strips, blocks, beans, buttons)

Objectives:

1. To add one object to a set to 5.

2. To add number facts to 5 vertically.

Teaching Pages 94 and 95:

1. Explain to the children that this is an important day. Today they will learn their first math operation. It is called *addition*. In today's lesson, they will add one object to the objects already in a set *up to* 5. Place four sets of blocks in front of the children—a set containing one block, a set containing two blocks, a set containing three blocks, and a set containing four blocks. Have the students count the number of blocks in each set. State that you are now going to add one block to each set.
Give the students one block and ask them to add it to the set of one.
Ask: "When I add this one block to the set, how many blocks are now in the set?" (2)
Give the students another block and ask them to add it to the set of two.
Ask: "When I add this one block to the set, how many blocks are now in the set?" (3)
Continue with the set of three and the set of four.

2. Have the students turn to page 94, and together read the directions at the top of the page. Point to the green block and explain that this represents the block in the set that they started with. Point to the blue block. Explain that this represents the block that they added. Ask them if the set they added is the same as the set on the page. (2) Call attention to the number fact in the center. Introduce the plus (+) sign and the line drawn below the two *1*'s. Explain that this is how we write a problem in addition. Read it aloud, "One plus one equals two." Point to the first *1* and say, "The set had one block in it." Point to the second *1* and say, "Then we added one block." Point to the number *2* and say, "Now the set has two blocks."
Ask: "How many blocks are in the next set?" (2) "Where is the number *2*?"
Point to its position in the problem. "How many did we add to the set?" (1)
"Where is the number *1* in the problem?" "Where is the sign that tells you to add?"
"How many blocks are in the new set?" (3) "Where is the number *3* in the problem?"
Use this same procedure to complete page 94.

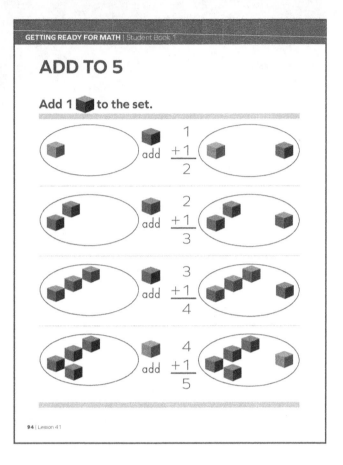

ADD TO 5

Add 1 ▪ to the set.

add	1 +1 / 2	
add	2 +1 / 3	
add	3 +1 / 4	
add	4 +1 / 5	

94 | Lesson 41

3. Turn to page 95. This page should be completed using the manipulatives (blocks, strips, beans, buttons). Beginning with the first problem, have the students look at the number *1* and take one object from the group of objects in front of them. Look at the second number *1* and the addition sign (+). Take another object from the group and add it to the first. Ask: "How many do you have altogether?" Then have the students write the number *2* as the answer to the first problem. Finally, have them read the problem: *One plus one equals two*. Proceed in this manner to complete the page.

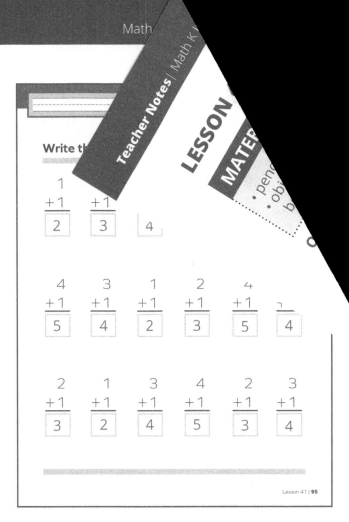

42

...RIALS NEEDED

...ils

...jects for counting (colored strips, blocks, ...eans, buttons)

...bjectives:

1. To add two objects to a set.

2. To add number facts to 5 vertically.

Teaching Pages 96 and 97:

1. Place three sets of blocks in front of the children—a set containing one block, a set containing two blocks, and a set containing three blocks. Have the students count the number of blocks in each set. State that you are now going to add two blocks to each set. Give the students two blocks and ask them to add them to the set of one. Ask: "When I add these two blocks to the set, how many blocks are now in the set?" (3) Give the students two more blocks and ask them to add them to the set of two. Ask: "When I add these two blocks to the set, how many blocks are now in the set?" (4) Continue with the set of three.

2. Have the students turn to page 96, and together read the directions at the top of the page. Point to the blue block and explain that this represents the block in the set that they started with. Point to the two brown blocks. Explain that this represents the blocks that they added. Ask them if their new set is the same as the set on the page. (3) Call attention to the number fact in the center. Review the plus (+) sign and the line drawn below the *1* and *2*. Explain that this is how we write a problem in addition. Read it aloud: *One plus two equals three*. Ask: "How many blocks are in the next set?" (2) "Where is the number *2*?" Point to its position in the problem. "How many did we add to the set?" (2) "Where is the number *2* in the problem?" "Where is the sign that tells you to add?" "How many blocks are in the new set?" (4) "Where is the number 4 in the problem?" Use this same procedure to complete page 96.

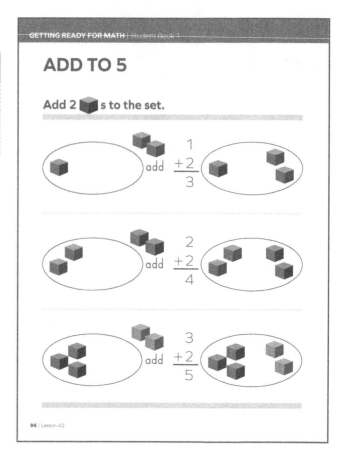

3. Turn to page 97. This page should be completed using the manipulatives (blocks, strips, beans). Beginning with the first problem, have the students look at the number *1* and take one object from the group of objects in front of them. Look at the second number *2* and the addition sign (+). Take two objects from the group and add them to the first. Ask: "How many do you have altogether?" Then have the students write the number 3 as the answer to the first problem. Finally, have them read the problem: *One plus two equals three*. Proceed slowly and in this manner to complete the page.

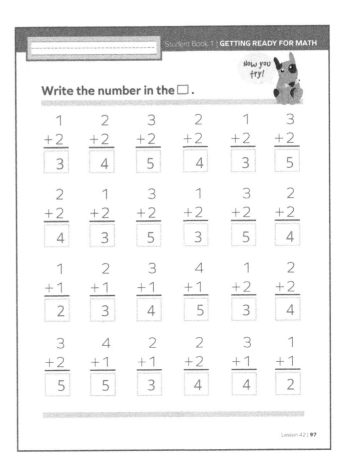

Student Book 1 | **GETTING READY FOR MATH**

Now you try!

Write the number in the ☐.

1	2	3	2	1	3
+2	+2	+2	+2	+2	+2
3	4	5	4	3	5

2	1	3	1	3	2
+2	+2	+2	+2	+2	+2
4	3	5	3	5	4

1	2	3	4	1	2
+1	+1	+1	+1	+2	+2
2	3	4	5	3	4

3	4	2	2	3	1
+2	+1	+1	+2	+1	+1
5	5	3	4	4	2

Lesson 42 | **97**

LESSON 43

MATERIALS NEEDED

- pencils
- objects for counting (colored strips, blocks, beans, buttons)

Objectives:

1. To add three and four objects to a set.

2. To add number facts to 5 vertically.

Teaching Pages 98 and 99:

1. Place three sets of blocks in front of the children—a set containing one block, a set containing two blocks, and a set containing one block. Have the students count the number of blocks in each set. Give the students three blocks and ask them to add them to the set of one. Ask: "When I add these three blocks to the set, how many blocks are now in the set?" (4) Give the students three more blocks and ask them to add them to the set of two. Ask: "When I add these two blocks to the set, how many blocks are now in the set?" (5) Give the students four blocks and ask them to add them to the set of one. Ask: "When I add these four blocks to the set, how many blocks are now in the set?" (5)

2. Have the students turn to page 98, and together read the directions at the top of the page. Point to the blue block and explain that this represents the block in the set that they started with. Point to the three brown blocks. Explain that they represent the blocks that they added. Ask them if their new set is the same as the set on the page. (4) Call attention to the number fact in the center. Review the plus (+) sign and the line drawn below the *1* and *3*. Explain that this is how we write a problem in addition. Read it aloud: *One plus three equals four.* Point to the first *1* and say, "The set had one block in it." Point to the *3* and say, "Then we added three blocks." Point to the number *4* and say, "Now the set has four blocks." Ask: "How many blocks are in the next set?" (2) "Where is the number *2*?" Point to its position in the problem. "How many did we add to the set?" (3) "Where is the number *3* in the problem?" "Where is the sign that tells you to add?" "How many blocks are in the new set?" (5) "Where is the number *5* in the problem?" Use this same procedure to complete page 98.

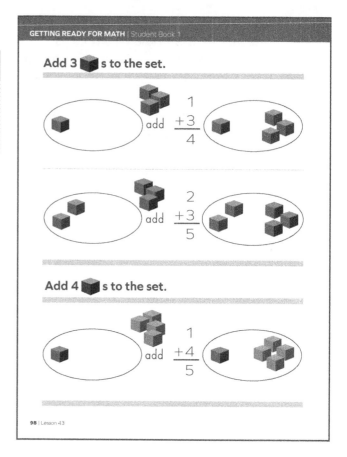

3. Turn to page 99. This page should be completed using the manipulatives (blocks, strips, beans, buttons). Beginning with the first problem, have the students look at the number *1* and take one object from the group of objects in front of them. Look at the second number *3* and the addition sign (+). Take three objects from the group and add them to the first. Ask: "How many do you have altogether?" Then have the students write the number *4* as the answer to the first problem. Finally, have them read the problem: *One plus three equals four*. Proceed slowly and in this manner to complete the page.

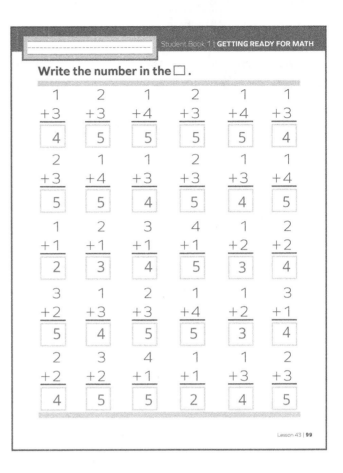

Student Book 1 | **GETTING READY FOR MATH**

Write the number in the ☐ .

1 +3 **4**	2 +3 **5**	1 +4 **5**	2 +3 **5**	1 +4 **5**	1 +3 **4**
2 +3 **5**	1 +4 **5**	1 +3 **4**	2 +3 **5**	1 +3 **4**	1 +4 **5**
1 +1 **2**	2 +1 **3**	3 +1 **4**	4 +1 **5**	1 +2 **3**	2 +2 **4**
3 +2 **5**	1 +3 **4**	2 +3 **5**	1 +4 **5**	1 +2 **3**	3 +1 **4**
2 +2 **4**	3 +2 **5**	4 +1 **5**	1 +1 **2**	1 +3 **4**	2 +3 **5**

Lesson 43 | **99**

101

LESSON 44

MATERIALS NEEDED

- pencils
- objects for counting (colored strips, blocks, beans, buttons)
- number cards and picture cards from Lesson 32

Objectives:

1. To add three and four objects to a set.

2. To add number facts to 5 vertically.

3. To use the colors through purple.

Teaching Pages 100 and 101:

1. Place a group of *5* objects in front of the students. Turn to page 100. Complete this page in the same manner as pages 97 and 99. Beginning with the first problem, have the students look at the number *1* and take one object from the group of objects in front of them. Look at the second number *1* and the addition sign (+). Take one object from the group and add it to the first. Have the students write the number *2* as the answer to the first problem. Finally, have them read the problem. *One plus one equals two.* The students should complete the page as independently as possible; however, it is important that each student read the problem aloud when completed.

2. Turn to page 101. Ask the children what Sam has in his paw? (bubble wand) Ask the students what the circles in the picture represent? (bubbles) Ask if the numbers are inside or outside of the bubbles? Do all the bubbles have numbers inside of them? Are there any numbers outside the bubbles? Ask what the numbers inside the bubbles represent? (problems in addition) Find the addition (plus) sign and the line drawn under the problem. Ask the children where they should write the answer to the

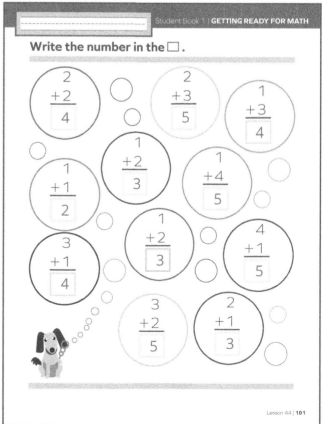

problem. To complete this page, each student should have a set of objects for counting in front of him. Have the children complete the page and then read each problem.

3. Use number cards and picture cards from Lesson 32 to play a game of concentration.

LESSON 45

MATERIALS NEEDED

- pencils
- objects for counting

Objectives:

1. To count the objects in sets.

2. To add number facts to 5 vertically.

Teaching Pages 102, 103, and 104:

1. This exercise will begin to develop the operation of addition as a concept. It should be treated as a game and may be played for several minutes as the children begin to understand what is being asked of them. Place a set of one block in front of the students. Do not give them another block but say to them: "If you added one block to this set, how many would you have?" If the students cannot give the correct response, give them one block and allow them to count *1-2*. Next give the students a set of two blocks. Do not give them another block but say to them: "If you added one block to this set, how many would you have?" Again, if the students cannot give the correct response, give them one block and allow them to count *1-2-3*. Continue this exercise for a few minutes using different combinations (3 + 2, 1 + 3). Ask the students to visualize (picture) the added blocks in their minds to help them develop the concept.

2. Turn to page 102. Call attention to the first set of clocks. Have the children count the clocks in the set aloud, pointing to each clock as they count. Then count the clock in the second set. Call attention to the number fact. Point to the *3* and state, "There are three objects in the first set." Point to the *1* and state, "There is one object in the second set." "Three plus one equals four." Have the class count all the objects in both sets. Point to the two sets at the bottom of the page. State that each set has two objects. Count the objects in both sets aloud, "One, two, three, four." Call attention to the number fact and read it aloud.

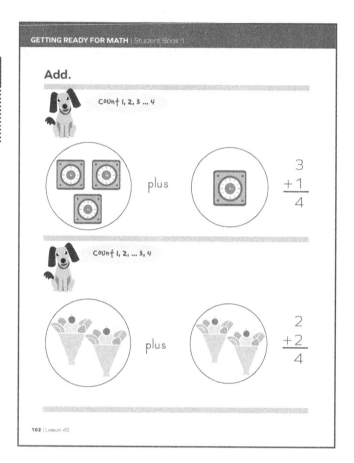

3. Turn to pages 103 and 104. Read the directions aloud. Point to the first box of sets. Have the class count the objects in the two sets aloud. Then have them write the number *5* in the box. Read the number fact aloud when it is complete. Repeat this procedure with the next box of sets. Allow the children to complete these pages independently.

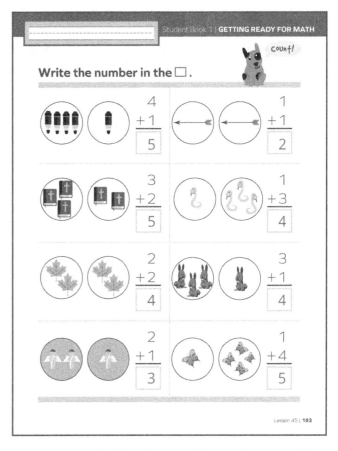

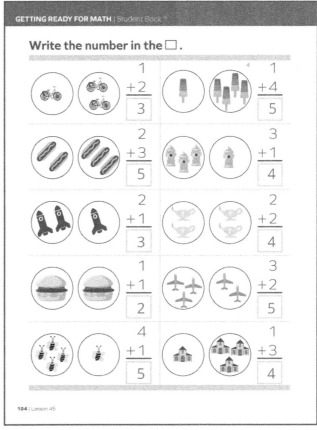

LESSON 46

MATERIALS NEEDED

- pencils
- objects for counting
- cutout pictures
- colored paper
- scissors
- paste or glue
- red, yellow, green, blue, brown, and purple crayons

Objectives:

1. To use colors and shapes to form sets.

2. To add number facts to 5 vertically.

Teaching Pages 105 and 106:

1. Play the game again that was introduced in Lesson 45. Begin with sets of *1*, *2*, *3*, or *4* objects and ask the children to add *1*, *2*, *3*, or *4* to them. Do not go over a total of *5*. If a student cannot visualize the correct response, immediately give him the additional objects for counting. Continue the game for several minutes.

2. Turn to pages 105 and 106. Let the students use cutout pictures, colored paper, or crayons to create shapes or pictures for their sets and paste or draw the objects on pages 105 and 106. If the objects are too large to fit on the worksheets, allow the students to complete the work on another piece of paper. Emphasize the use of the colors and shapes (circles, triangles, squares, rectangles) that they have learned. They may use any shapes and objects as their imaginations allow them. Call attention to the addition problems. Have the students complete the problems and read them orally.

3. Be sure the students understand the correlation between their pictures and the number facts.

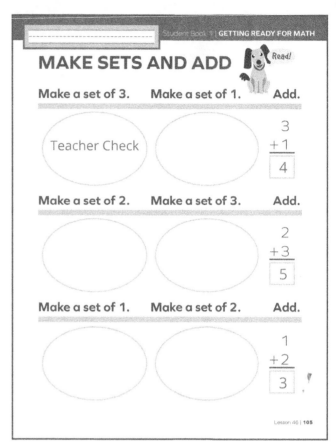

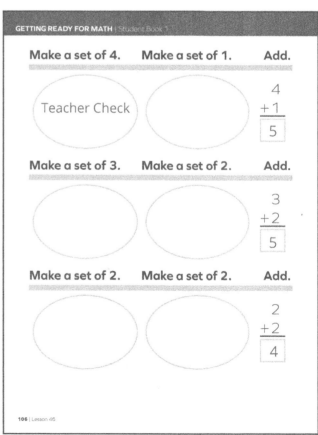

LESSON 47

MATERIALS NEEDED

- pencils
- objects for counting (colored strips, blocks, beans, buttons)

Objectives:

1. To add number facts to 5 vertically.

2. To write the numbers before and after.

Teaching Pages 107, 108, and 109:

1. Turn to page 107. Read the directions, and have the students complete the first exercise. They may count the objects in the sets to complete the addition problems. Have the students look at the vertical number facts (addition problems) at the bottom of the page. Complete the first problem by placing one block in front of the students. Have them look at the problem and ask: "How many should you add to one?" (3) Then ask the students for the correct answer to the problem. If they can visualize the answer, have them write it down. If not, they may use the objects for counting (1-2-3-4). Continue in this manner for the remainder of the problems on the page.

2. Turn to pages 108 and 109. Read the title of page 108. Talk about the illustrations on pages 108 and 109 until the students are familiar with them. Have the students read the numbers at the top of the page, and read the words *Before* and *After* to them. Start at the first picture on page 108. Have the students count the number of birds. (4) Ask them what number comes before *4*. (3) (They may use the numbers at the top of the page for number order.) Show them that the number *3* is written on the line under *Before*. Have them count the number of birds again. (4) Ask the children what number comes after *4*. (5) (Again, let them

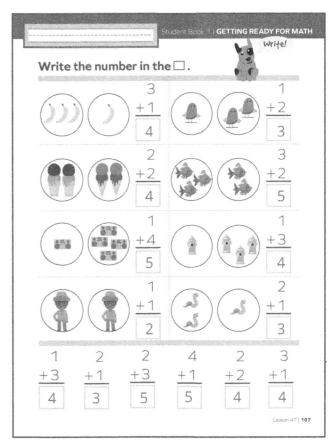

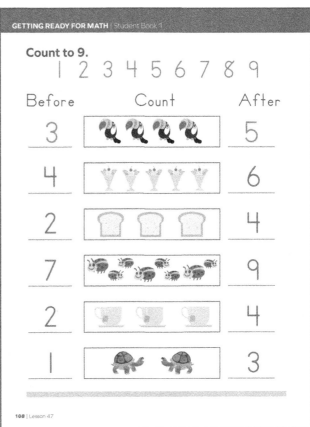

use the numbers at the top of the page for number order.) Show them that the number *5* is written on the line under *After*. Have the students complete pages 108 and 109 as independently as possible. Remind them to use good posture, to hold their pencil correctly, and to follow the rules they have learned to write their numbers.

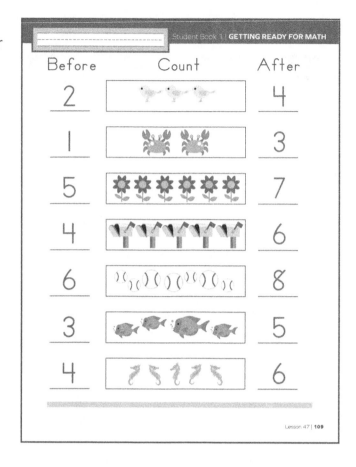

LESSON 48

MATERIALS NEEDED

- pencils
- objects for counting

Objectives:

1. To add one object to a set to 9.

2. To add number facts to 9 vertically.

Teaching Pages 110 and 111:

1. In today's lesson, the children will add one object to the objects in a set *up to* nine. Place four sets of objects in front of the children—a set containing five objects, a set containing six objects, a set containing seven objects, and a set containing eight objects. Have the students count the number of objects in each set. State that you are now going to add one object to each set. Give the students one object and ask them to add it to the set of five. Ask: "When I add this one object to the set, how many objects are now in the set?" (6) Give the students another object and ask them to add it to the set of six. Ask: "When I add this one object to the set, how many objects are now in the set?" (7) Continue with the set of seven and the set of eight.

2. Have the students turn to page 110 and together read the directions at the top of the page. Point to the green blocks and explain that they represent the objects in the set that they started with. Point to the blue block. Explain that this represents the block that they added. Ask them if their new set is the same as the set on the page. (6) Call attention to the number fact in the center. Review the plus (+) sign and the line drawn below the *5* and *1*. Read it aloud, "Five plus one equals six." Point to the *5* and say, "The set had five blocks in it." Point to the *1* and say, "Then we added one block." Point to the number *6* and say, "Now the set has six blocks." Ask: "How many blocks are in the next set?" (6) "Where is the number *6*?" Point to its position in the problem. "How many did we add to the set?" (1) "Where is the number *1* in the problem?" "Where is the sign that tells you to add?" "How many blocks are in the new set?" (7) "Where is the number *7* in the problem?" Use this same procedure to complete page 110.

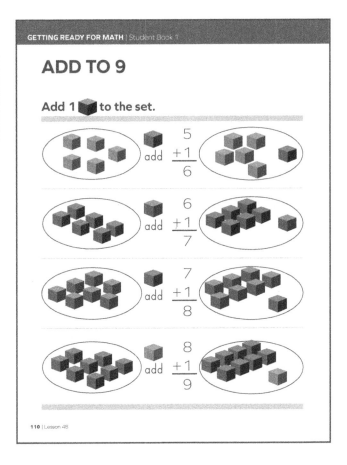

3. Turn to page 111. This page should be completed using the manipulatives (blocks, strips, beans). Beginning with the first problem, have the students look at the number *5*, the number *1*, and the addition sign (+). Tell the students to make two sets that represent the problem. Then ask: "How many do you have altogether?" (6) Have the students write the number *6* as the answer to the first problem. Finally, have them read the problem. *Five plus one equals six.* Proceed in this manner to complete the page.

LESSON 49

MATERIALS NEEDED

- pencils
- objects for counting

Objectives:

1. To add two objects to a set.

2. To add number facts to 9 vertically.

Teaching Pages 112 and 113:

1. Place four sets of objects in front of the children—a set containing four objects, a set containing five objects, a set containing six objects, and a set containing seven objects. Have the students count the number of objects in each set. State that you are now going to add two objects to each set. Give the students two objects, and ask them to add them to the set of four. Ask: "When I add these two objects to the set, how many objects are now in the set?" (6) Give the students two more objects and ask them to add them to the set of five. Ask: "When I add these two objects to the set, how many objects are now in the set?" (7) Continue with the sets of six and seven.

2. Have the students turn to page 112, and together read the directions at the top of the page. Point to the four blue blocks, and explain that they represent the objects in the set that they started with. Point to the two brown blocks. Explain that they represent the blocks that they added. Ask them if their new set is the same as the set on the page. (6) Call attention to the number fact in the center. Review the plus (+) sign and the line drawn below the *4* and *2*. Read the number fact aloud, "Four plus two equals six." Point to the *4* and say, "The set had four blocks in it." Point to the *2* and say, "Then we added two blocks." Point to the number *6* and say, "Now the set has six blocks." Ask: "How many blocks are in the next set?" (5) "Where is the number *5*?" Point to its position in the problem. "How many did we add to the set?" (2) "Where is the number *2* in the problem?" "Where is the sign that tells you to add?" "How many blocks are in the new set?" (7) "Where is the number *7* in the problem?" Use this same procedure to complete page 112.

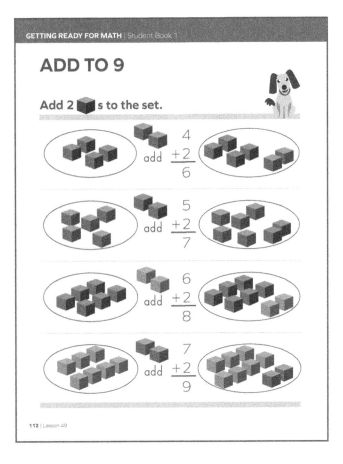

GETTING READY FOR MATH | Student Book 1

ADD TO 9

Add 2 ◼s to the set.

add +2 / 4 / 6

add +2 / 5 / 7

add +2 / 6 / 8

add +2 / 7 / 9

112 | Lesson 49

3. Turn to page 113. This page should be completed using the manipulatives (blocks, strips, beans). Beginning with the first problem, have the students look at the number *4*, the number *2*, and the addition sign (+). Tell the students to make two sets that represent the problem. Then ask: "How many do you have altogether?" (6) Have the students write the number *6* as the answer to the first problem. Finally, have them read the problem. *Four plus two equals six*. Proceed in this manner to complete the page.

Student Book 1 | **GETTING READY FOR MATH**

Now you try!

Write the number in the ☐ .

4	5	6	7	4	6
+2	+2	+2	+2	+2	+2
6	7	8	9	6	8

5	7	6	4	5	7
+2	+2	+2	+2	+2	+2
7	9	8	6	7	9

5	6	7	8	4	5
+1	+1	+1	+1	+2	+2
6	7	8	9	6	7

6	7	3	2	1	4
+2	+2	+2	+2	+2	+1
8	9	5	4	3	5

Lesson 49 | **113**

LESSON 50

MATERIALS NEEDED

• pencils
• objects for counting

Objectives:

1. To add three objects to a set.

2. To add number facts to 9 vertically.

Teaching Pages 114 and 115:

1. Review the students' ability to do mental addition. Remember, it should be treated as a game and should be played for only a short period of time. Review the addition facts through *5*. Place a set of *4* objects in front of the students. Do not give them another object but say to them: "If you added one object to this set, how many would you have?" If the students cannot give the correct response, give them one block and allow them to count *1-2-3-4-5*. Next, give the students a set of one object. Do not give them any objects but say to them: "If you added three objects to this set, how many would you have?" Again, if the students cannot give the correct response, give them three objects and allow them to count *1-2-3-4*. Continue this exercise for a few minutes using different combinations. Ask the students to visualize the added objects in their minds to help them develop a mental picture of the number fact.

2. Turn to page 114. Use the objects as manipulatives to illustrate each exercise on page 114. Call the students' attention to the number facts in the center of the page. Have the students read each fact aloud before going on to the next example.

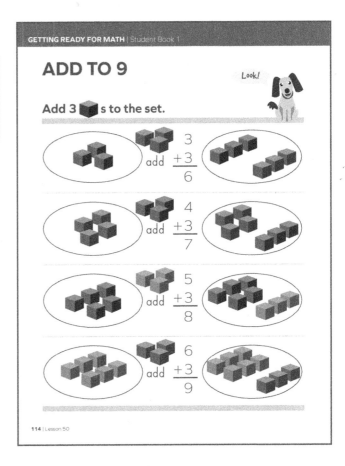

3. Turn to page 115. Ask the students to read the problem. (3 plus 3) Tell the students to make two sets of *3* and add them together. (6) Write the answer below the line. Read the problem again. (3 plus 3 equals 6.) Proceed in the same manner to complete page 115.

Write the number in the ☐ .

3	4	5	6	4	6
+3	+3	+3	+3	+3	+3
6	7	8	9	7	9
5	3	6	3	3	3
+3	+3	+3	+5	+4	+6
8	6	9	8	7	9
5	6	7	8	4	5
+1	+1	+1	+1	+2	+2
6	7	8	9	6	7
6	7	3	4	5	6
+2	+2	+3	+3	+3	+3
8	9	6	7	8	9
2	1	3	4	2	1
+3	+2	+2	+1	+2	+3
5	3	5	5	4	4

MATH KINDERGARTEN

Lessons 51–60

LESSON 51

MATERIALS NEEDED

- pencils
- objects for counting

Objectives:

1. To add four objects to a set.

2. To add number facts to 9 vertically.

Teaching Pages 116 and 117:

1. Review the addition facts through *9*. Give the students any set of objects up to seven. Ask them to add one, two, or three to the different sets. (Do not exceed a total of *9*.) Encourage them to picture the objects in their minds before giving the answer. Continue to give them the objects for counting if necessary to achieve the correct answer. Spend several minutes on this exercise. As they are able to answer more each day without using the objects for counting, let them know that they are making good progress.

2. Turn to page 116. Tell the students that today they will learn to add *4* to a set. Use the objects as manipulatives to illustrate each exercise on page 116. Call the students' attention to the number facts in the center of the page. Have the students read each fact aloud before going on to the next example.

3. Turn to page 117. Ask the students to read the problem. (2 plus 4) Tell the students to make a set of 2 and a set of 4 and add them together. (6) Write the answer below the line. Read the problem again. (2 plus 4 equals 6.) Proceed in the same manner to complete page 117.

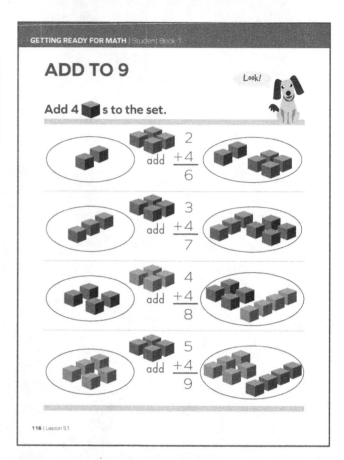

LESSON 52

MATERIALS NEEDED

- pencils
- objects for counting
- red, yellow, green, blue, brown, and purple crayons

Objectives:

1. To add number facts to 9 vertically.

2. To use the colors through purple.

Teaching Pages 118 and 119:

1. Turn to page 118. Ask the students to read the numbers at the top of the page. Tell them that this is a page of addition facts. Ask them to read the first problem. Place five objects in front of the students, and ask how many they would have if they added one to the set of five. (6) Have the students find the number *six* at the top of the page, and have them write the *six* in the box. Proceed in this way to complete the page. Always begin by using objects to represent the first number, and ask the students to add the second number. For example, if the problem is five plus four, place five objects in front of the students. Ask them how many they would have if they added four. (9) Have them locate the 9 at the top of the page, and then write it in the answer box. If the students cannot visualize the answer for *5* plus *4*, have them take an additional *4* objects for counting.

2. Turn to page 119. Read the title to the children, and have them answer the questions. Tell them to color the picture using the colors in the boxes. Have them name the colors before they begin.

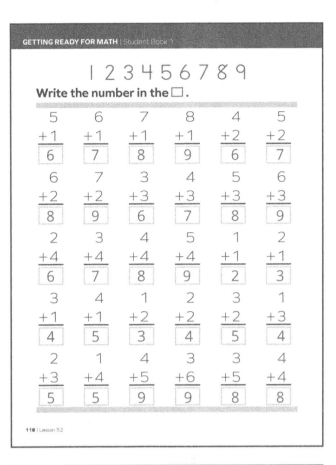

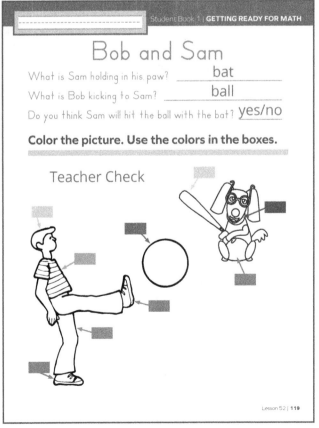

LESSON 53

MATERIALS NEEDED

- pencils
- objects for counting
- red, yellow, blue, green, brown, and purple crayons

Objectives:

1. To make sets to equal number facts.

2. To add number facts to 9 vertically.

3. To write number symbols to 9.

Teaching Pages 120 and 121:

1. Place *nine* objects in a row so that the students may refer to them for counting. Place a set of *two* objects in front of the students. Ask them to make a set of *four* objects beginning with the set of *two* objects. Ask them how large a set they will need to add to a set of *two* to make a set of *four*. Let them refer to the objects that are set out for counting. The students should decide that it takes *two* objects to add to *two* to make a set of *four*. Tell them to say the number fact: *two plus two equals four*. Put this set aside. Give the students a set of *four* objects. Ask them to make a set of *seven* objects beginning with the set of *four*. Ask them how large a set they will need to add to the set of *four* to make a set of *seven*. The students should decide that it takes *three* objects to add to *four* to make a set of *seven*. Tell them to say the number fact: *four plus three equals seven*. Put this set aside. Use the same procedure starting with a set of one object and making a set of *five*, a set of *eight* objects and making a set of *nine*, a set of *six* objects and making a set of *eight*, a set of *two* objects and making a set of *six*. Turn to page 120. Read the directions. Have the children refer to the sets that they have just completed as they write the answers to the number facts.

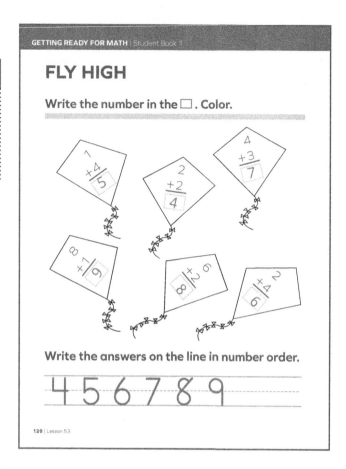

2. Turn to page 121. Read the directions at the bottom of the page and ask the children to use good posture and to hold their pencils correctly to write the numbers *1* to *9*. Read the directions at the top of the page. Ask the children to read the number facts (problems) aloud (four plus two) and write the answer in the box. (They may use objects to solve the problems.) When the work is completed let them color pages 120 and 121. Use only the colors they have learned about.

LESSON 54

MATERIALS NEEDED

- pencils
- paper

Objectives:

1. To write number facts to 9.

2. To add number facts to 9 vertically.

Teaching Pages 122 and 123:

1. Each student should have a pencil and a piece of paper and should be sitting with good posture and holding the pencil correctly. Dictate the following problems to the students (including answers). Be sure that they form numbers correctly, that they use the addition (plus) sign, and that they draw the line between the problem and the answer. Give them enough time to do the exercise neatly. Have the children read the problems aloud after they have written each of them on paper.

2. Dictate: (five plus three equals eight)

$$\begin{array}{ccccc} 5 & 2 & 6 & 1 & 7 \\ +\ 3 & +\ 4 & +\ 1 & +\ 5 & +\ 2 \\ \hline 8 & 6 & 7 & 6 & 9 \end{array}$$

3. Turn to pages 122 and 123. Point to the first box of sets on page 122. Have the children count the objects in the two sets aloud. Tell them to write the answer in the box beneath the number fact and to read the number fact aloud. Read the directions aloud for page 123. Explain to the children that they will do the same activity on this page that they did on page 122.

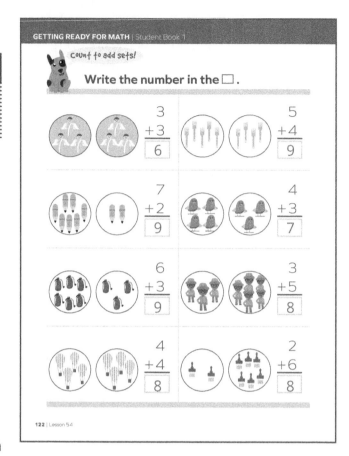

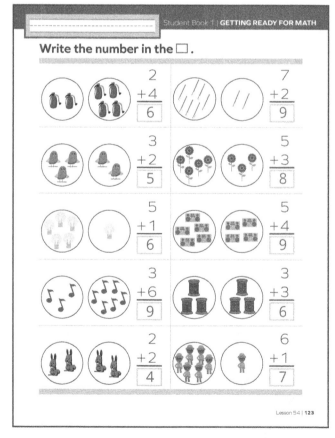

LESSON 55

MATERIALS NEEDED

- pencils
- paper
- objects for counting
- sample cutouts of a triangle, a square, and a rectangle
- red, yellow, green, blue, brown, and purple crayons

Objectives:

1. To illustrate shapes using color.

2. To add number facts to 9 vertically.

3. To write the missing number.

4. To say the ordinal (order) numbers.

Teaching Pages 124 and 125:

1. Place nine objects in front of the students and ask them to count the objects (1-2-3-4-5-6-7-8-9).

2. Turn to page 124. Read the instructions and show the cutout shapes to the students. Be sure they know the name of each one. Have the students complete the page by tracing around the outside of the sample cutouts using the correct color. Students may draw their sets on another piece of paper if they need more space. Tell the students to write the answer to the number fact and then say it aloud.

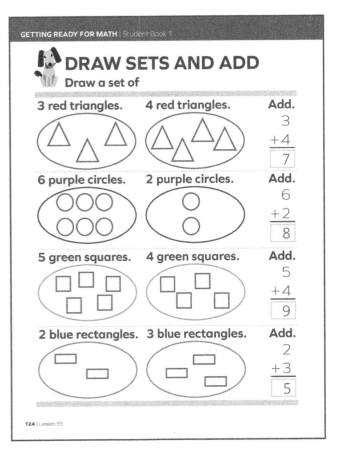

3. Turn to page 125. Ask the students to look at the numbers in each circle and say them aloud. Ask them to draw a square around the number as you say its name. (Circle 1: six, Circle 2: four, Circle 3: eight, Circle 4: one, Circle 5: nine, Circle 6: three) Read the next set of instructions. Have the students fill in the missing numbers. Let them use the nine objects that you have set out for counting. Ask the students to count the triangles at the bottom of the page (1-2-3-4-5-6-7-8-9). Review order counting with them (first, second, third, fourth, fifth, sixth, seventh, eighth, ninth). Have the students describe each triangle as "This is the first triangle," "This is the second triangle," and so on to the ninth. Describe a triangle by color and ask the students to point to the corresponding triangle (or triangles).

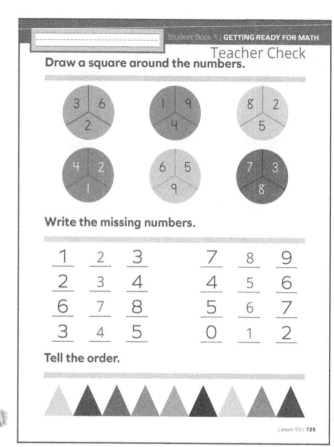

LESSON 56

MATERIALS NEEDED

- pencils
- crayons
- alphabet charts

Objectives:

1. To understand position words.

2. To recognize the positions of objects.

3. To complete part of the alphabet in the correct order.

Teaching Pages 126 and 127:

1. Turn to page 126. Place nine objects in front of the students. Ask the students to read the first problem (one plus two). Tell them to illustrate the problem by using objects to make sets (one set of one and one set of two). Ask them to give the answer to one plus two and then write the answer in the box. Complete the first three rows of problems in this manner using objects for counting. Continue the fourth row by giving the students two objects and asking them how many objects they would have if they added five objects to the set. (Do not give them the objects at this time.) Allow the students time to visualize the answer. If they cannot, they may use additional objects for counting.

2. Turn to page 127. Help the children read "Climb the Steps!" Ask them to find the steps in the picture and to find the problems. Use manipulatives to help the students complete the page. Those students who wish to may go on to color this page. Ask where they would find steps (house). Let them draw a picture of a house putting steps on the front of the house or on the inside. Complete the drawing adding other objects and using the colors that they have learned.

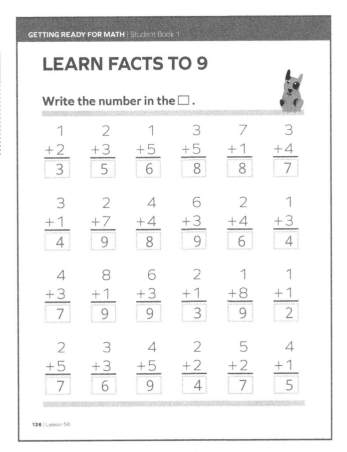

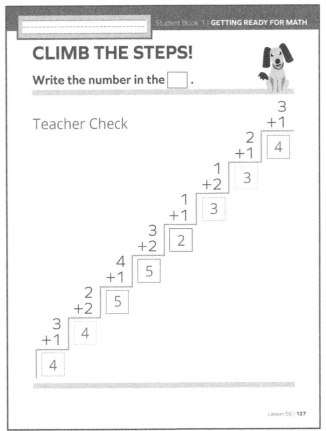

LESSON 57

MATERIALS NEEDED

- pencils
- objects for counting
- red, yellow, green, blue, brown, and purple crayons

Objectives:

1. To add number facts to 9 vertically.

2. To say the ordinal (order) numbers.

3. To illustrate by using the colors to purple.

Teaching Pages 128 and 129:

1. Turn to page 128. Read the instructions aloud. The students may use objects for counting to solve the number facts at the bottom of the page.

2. Turn to page 129. Talk to the children about the illustrations in the picture. Have them give the order of the clocks, sodas (first, second, third). Tell them to count "how many" (ducks, clocks, sodas, fish, and so on).

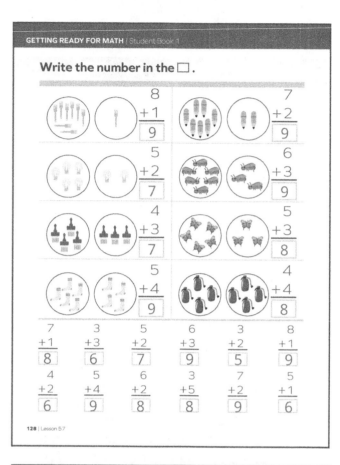

LESSON 58

MATERIALS NEEDED

- pencils
- objects for counting

Objective:

To add number facts to 9 vertically.

Teaching Pages 130 and 131:

1. Turn to page 130. Read the instructions aloud. Have the children count the number in each set. (3,3) Point to the numbers in the number fact. (3,3) Ask the children what the sign (+) is telling them to do and have them write the answer in the box. (6) Allow the children to complete the page independently.

2. Turn to page 131. Place a group of nine objects in front of the children. Ask the children what this page contains. (number facts) Read the directions and have the children work the first problem. Then have them read the problem aloud. Allow the children to complete the page independently. The children may use the objects for counting if necessary.

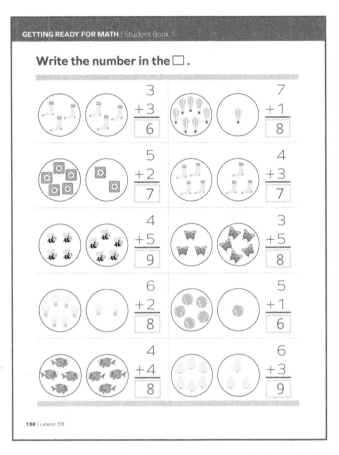

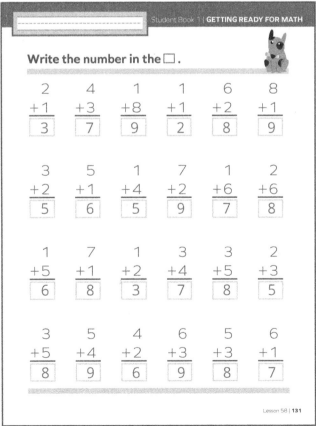

LESSON 59

MATERIALS NEEDED

- pencils
- objects for counting
- addition fact cards on 2-inch by 3-inch card-board for 1's (1 + 1, 1 + 2, 1 + 3, 1 + 4, 1 + 5, 1 + 6, 1 + 7, 1 + 8), (a double set of fact cards may be made—one without answers on the back so they may be used for later games of concentration)
- red, yellow, green, blue, brown, purple, and orange crayons

Objectives:

1. To add number facts to 9 vertically.

2. To write the numbers between.

3. To learn the color orange.

Teaching Pages 132, 133, and 134:

1. Introduce the fact cards using sets of objects so that the students understand the meaning of the fact cards. In the beginning, present them to the students in number order. When the students become proficient, the order may be mixed. Spend only a short time on this exercise.

2. Turn to page 132. Read the directions. Explain to the students that these are number facts like the facts on their new fact cards. Tell the students that they may use objects for counting or their new fact cards to complete the problems.

3. Turn to page 133. Tell the students to read the numbers at the top of the page. Read the directions. Ask the students to count the number of clocks in the first set. (3) Ask the students to count the number of clocks in the second set. (6) Tell them to look at the numbers at the top of the page. Ask them to point to the numbers that are missing between *3* and *6*. Tell them to write the numbers. Continue in this manner to complete the page.

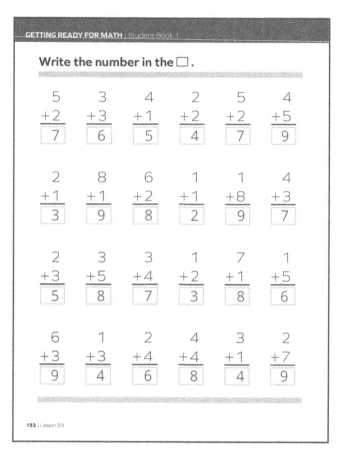

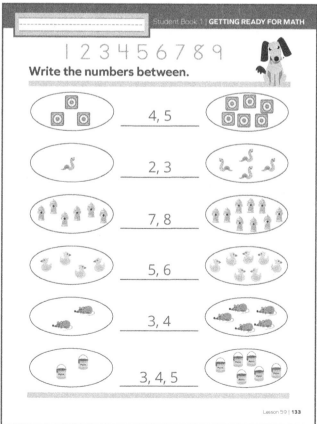

4. Turn to page 134. Ask the students to point to the boxes at the top of the page and name the first six colors. Introduce the color orange to them. Ask them where they might find the color orange. (pumpkin, orange) Ask them to draw a picture using a pumpkin or an orange. (orange tree, glass of orange juice, pumpkin in a field, pumpkin pie) Use the other colors to complete the drawings adding as much detail to the picture as the children would like.

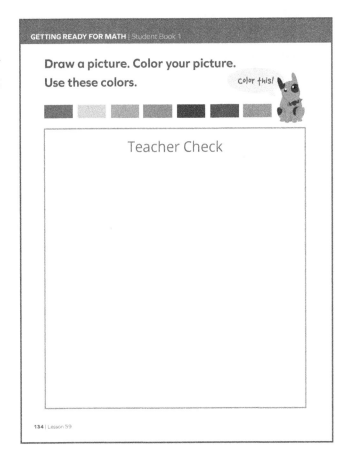

LESSON 60

MATERIALS NEEDED

- pencils
- objects for counting
- addition fact cards for 1's and 2's (2 + 1, 2 + 2, 2 + 3, 2 + 4, 2 + 5, 2 + 6, 2 + 7)
- red, yellow, green, blue, brown, purple, and orange crayons

Objectives:

1. To add number facts to 9 vertically.

2. To write the numbers between.

3. To review colors and shapes.

Teaching Pages 135, 136, and 137:

1. Review the fact cards for 1's. Make two sets of addition fact cards (one without answers) for 2's and introduce them to the students using sets of objects. Present them to the students in number order at the beginning. When the students become proficient, the order may be mixed. Spend only a short time on this exercise.

2. Turn to page 135. Read the directions. Explain to the students that this is a page of number facts like their fact cards. Tell the students that they may use objects for counting or their new fact cards to complete the facts.

3. Turn to page 136. Ask the students to read the numbers at the top of the page. Read the directions. Ask the student to count the number of birds in the first set. (2) Ask the students to count the number of birds in the second set. (8) Tell them to look at the numbers at the top of the page. Ask them to point to the number(s) that are missing between *2* and *8*. Tell them to write the number(s). Continue in this manner to complete the page.

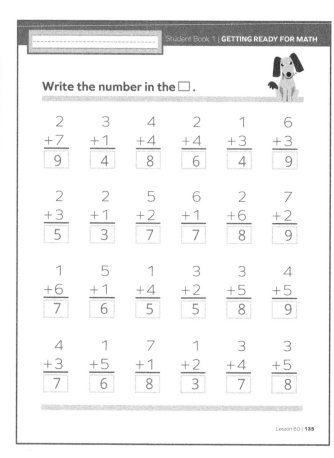

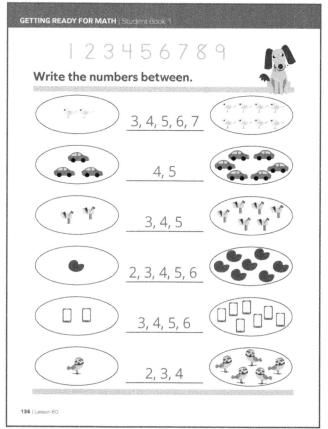

4. Turn to page 137. Read the directions at the top of the page. Ask the students to name the shapes in the first column; then, ask them to name the colors. Ask them to find the same shapes in the second column. Tell them to match the shapes one-to-one (draw a line) and then color the shapes in the second column so they are the same color as the shapes in the first column.

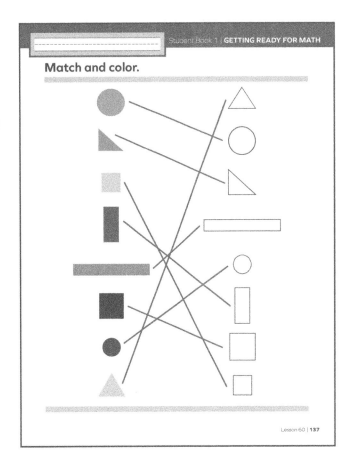

MATH KINDERGARTEN

Lessons 61–70

LESSON 61

MATERIALS NEEDED

• pencils

Objectives:

1. To recognize the number word that goes with the number symbol.

2. To write the number words one to five.

Teaching Pages 138, 139, and 140:

1. Turn to page 138. Read the title and have the children point to the first set. Have the children count the number of ice cream cones in the first set. Point to the number *1* and state, "There is one ice cream cone." Point to the third column and state, "This is the number *1* and this is the number word *one*." Repeat this procedure for each of the remaining sets on page 138. Then ask the children to read the list of number words. Have the children put their fingers on the letters and trace the words by tracing each letter.

2. Turn to page 139. Read the directions aloud. Have the children count the number of pigs in the first set (3) and have them find the number (3) at the top of the page. Tell them to write the number in the box. Allow the children to complete the page independently.

GETTING READY FOR MATH | Student Book 1

SETS, NUMBERS, WORDS 1 TO 5

Read!

Look	Count	Write
	I	1 one
	I, 2	2 two
	I, 2, 3	3 three
	I, 2, 3, 4	4 four
	I, 2, 3, 4, 5	5 five

138 | Lesson 61

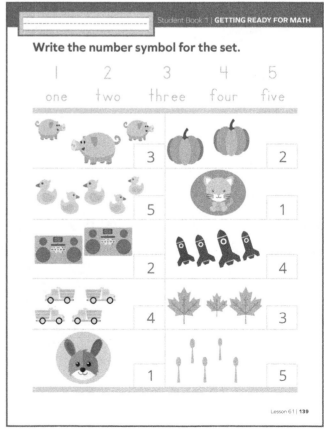

Student Book 1 | **GETTING READY FOR MATH**

Write the number symbol for the set.

1	2	3	4	5
one	two	three	four	five

Lesson 61 | **139**

3. Turn to page 140. Read the instructions aloud. Have the children point to the number words at the top of the page and say them aloud. Ask the children to count the number of candies in the first set and find the number *2* at the top of the page. Have them write the word *two* on the line. The children should go on to complete the page. Care should be taken that they are identifying the numbers correctly and following the correct procedures to write the number words.

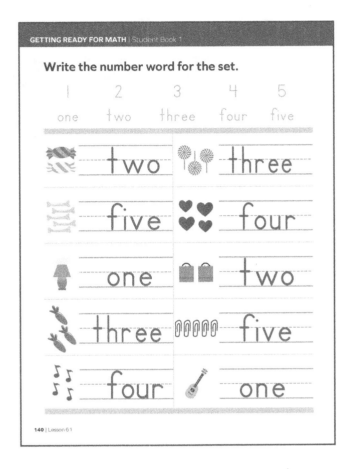

LESSON 62

MATERIALS NEEDED

• pencils

Objectives:

1. To recognize the number word that goes with the number symbol.

2. To write the number words one to five.

Teaching Pages 141, 142, and 143:

1. Turn to page 138. Ask the students to read the numbers and number words and trace the letters with their fingers. Turn to page 141. Read the directions at the top of the page. Have the children count the ducks in the first set. Point to the number *3*. Have the children write the number word. Encourage them to write their letters using proper procedures. Complete the page.

2. Turn to page 142. Read the title aloud. Have the children point to the first set and count the number of raindrops in the set. Have them count the numbers *1* to *6*. Point to the number *6* and state, "This is the number *6* and this is the number word *six*." Repeat this procedure for each of the remaining sets on page 142. Ask the students to read each one of the number words. Have the children put their fingers on the letters and trace the words by tracing each letter.

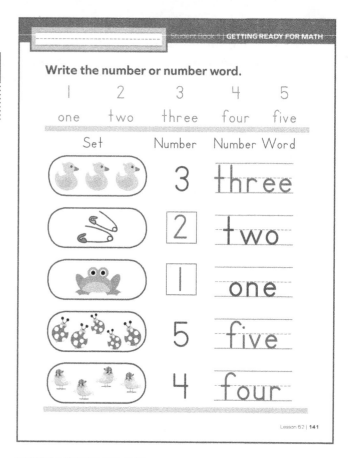

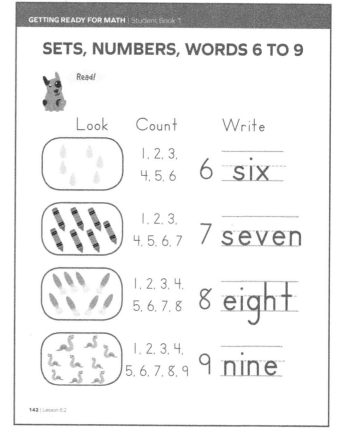

3. Turn to page 143. Have the children count the moons in the first set (8) and identify the number (8) at the top of the page. Tell them to write the number *8* in the box. Allow them to complete the page independently.

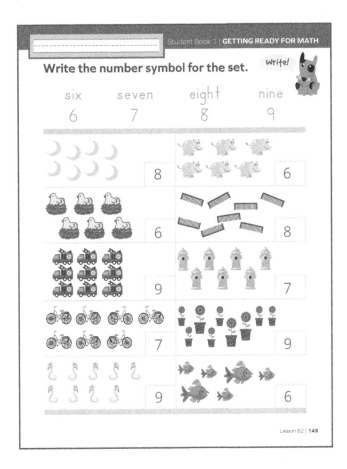

LESSON 63

MATERIALS NEEDED

- pencils
- objects for counting
- fact cards for 1's and 2's

Objectives:

1. To write the number words six through nine.

2. To learn the facts for 1's and 2's.

Teaching Pages 144 and 145:

1. Turn to page 142. Ask the children to read the number words six through nine and trace the letters with their fingers. Turn to page 144. Have the children count the number of globes in the first set (6) and find the number word at the top of the page. Have the children write the number word and then complete the page. Encourage them to write their letters using proper procedures.

2. Turn to page 145. Have the children count the fish in the first set and point to the number *8*. Have the children find the number word (eight) at the top of the page and write it on the line. The children should go on to complete the page. Care should be taken that they are identifying the numbers correctly and following the proper procedures to write the number words.

3. Review addition facts for *1's* and *2's*. Place nine objects so that the students can reach them. Give the first fact card *1 + 2* to the students and ask them if they know the answer to the fact. (3) Ask them to make sets illustrating the fact card. Ask them if they have the same answer to *1 + 2 =* . (3) Continue in this manner through the *1's* and *2's* until all fact cards have been used. Mix the fact cards and test the students ability to give the answer without use of manipulatives. Have them visualize the answer. On those facts that cause difficulty, allow them to use the objects for counting.

1's threw 12
2's threw 10

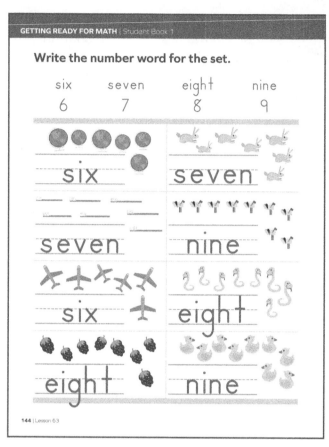

LESSON 64

MATERIALS NEEDED

- pencils
- objects for counting
- red, yellow, green, blue, brown, purple, and orange crayons

Objectives:

1. To write the number word.

2. To recognize and write the number symbol for zero.

Teaching Pages 146 and 147:

— by herself

1. Turn to page 146. Have the students read the number symbols and number words at the top of the page. Read the directions aloud. Point to the first box and ask the children to count the number of clowns. Show them the box for writing the number symbol (2) and the lines for writing the number word (two). The children may complete the page independently. Care should be taken that they are identifying the numbers correctly and following the proper procedures to write the number words.

none nothing empty

2. Place nine objects in front of the students and ask them to count them. Remove the objects from the table. Ask: "Now how many objects?" Elicit responses of *none*, *empty*, and *zero*. Ask the children if they know how to write *none*, *empty*, and *zero*.

3. Turn to page 147. Ask the children if they see a shape that looks familiar to them. (The zero can be compared to a circle.) Explain to the children that this shape is a number symbol that stands for *nothing*. It means that whatever group or set we are talking about has *none* there. Tell them the name of the number symbol is *zero*. Ask them to point to the outline of the set. Ask: "How many objects are in the set?" (zero or none) Point to the number word *zero*. Tell the children that this is how we spell the

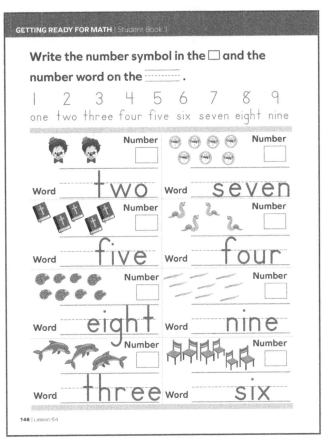

word *zero*. Ask the children to draw an empty set, to write the number symbol *0*, and to write the number word *zero*. Have the children look at the pond. Ask: "How many ducks do you see?" Have the children point to the *0* and say, "Zero ducks because there are no ducks in the pond." Allow the children to color the pond using the colors that they have learned.

didn't want to color

LESSON 65

MATERIALS NEEDED

- pencils
- paper
- objects for counting
- new fact cards for zero (0 + 1, 0 + 2, 0 + 3, 0 + 4, 0 + 5, 0 + 6, 0 + 7, 0 + 8, 0 + 9)

Objectives:

1. To write the number symbol for the set.

2. To add zero to numbers 1 through 9.

Teaching Pages 148 and 149:

1. Place a group of objects in front of the students. Ask them to count the number of objects in the set and write the number on the paper. Remove the objects and ask the student, "How many objects now?" (zero, nothing, none) Tell the students to write the number symbol that stands for (zero or nothing) on the paper. (0) Do this with several groups of objects of varying sizes.

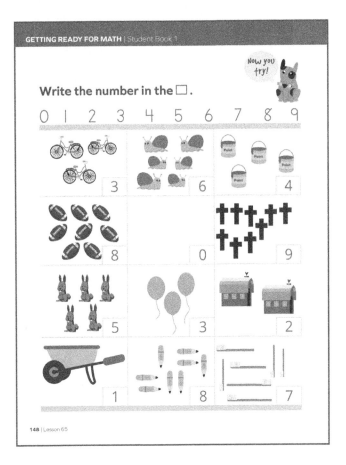

2. Turn to page 148. Have the students read the numbers at the top of the page. Show them the position of zero in number order. Ask them to point to the first set and count the tricycles. (3) Have them find the number symbol at the top of the page and write the symbol in the box. Continue in this manner to complete the page.

3. Place a group of *9* objects within reach of the students. Be sure there is nothing directly in front of them. Tell them there is a set in front of them. Ask them to describe the set. (Empty, nothing, zero). Tell them to write the number symbol for this set on the piece of paper.

4. Give the students one object and ask them to add it to the set. Ask them how many objects they have now. (0 + 1 = 1) Ask them to write the number *1* on the piece of paper. Continue doing this through *9*, beginning each time with an empty set.

5. Turn to page 149. Use this page to review the steps that the children have gone through with the manipulatives. Have them read the number facts at the bottom of the page. Introduce them to the zero (0) fact cards and have them give responses to the fact cards several times. For those students having difficulty, start with an empty set and use the objects for counting.

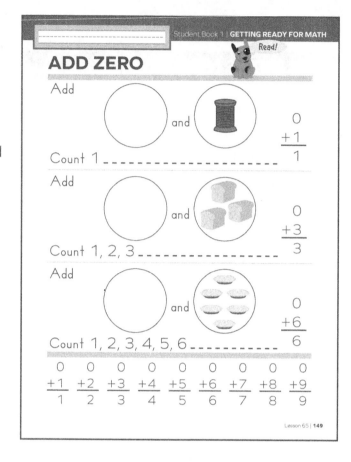

LESSON 66

MATERIALS NEEDED

- pencils
- paper
- objects for counting
- fact cards for 0's, 1's, 2's
- new fact cards (1 + 0, 2 + 0, 3 + 0, 4 + 0, 5 + 0, 6 + 0, 7 + 0, 8 + 0, 9 + 0)

Objectives:

1. To write the number symbol for the set.

2. To add zero to numbers 1 through 9.

Teaching Pages 150 and 151:

1. Review the sets of fact cards for 0's, 1's, and 2's, and then place them within reach of the students.

2. Place the new set of fact cards in front of the students. Have them take *1* object from the group of objects. Ask them to add zero (nothing) to it. Ask them how many objects they have now. (1) Point to the fact card and have them say *1 plus 0 equals 1*. Use the word *zero* with the children to develop good habits. Have the students take two objects from the group and ask them to add zero to them. Ask how many objects they have now. (2) Point to the fact card and have them say *two plus 0 equals 2*. Proceed in this manner until all fact cards are used. Place the *1 + 0* card with the group of *1's* fact cards and the *2 + 0* with the *2's* fact cards. Set the remainder aside and use as the other fact sets for *3-4-5-6-7-8-9* are introduced.

3. Turn to page 150. Read the directions aloud. Tell the children to point to the exercise. State that there are two sets. Ask the children to count the number of objects in the first set and look at the number fact. Have them count the number in the second set and look at the number fact again. Ask them the meaning of the plus sign. (add) Have the children write the answer to the fact. (3) Have them complete this part of the page independently. Tell them to look at the number facts at the bottom of the page. Ask them if they have seen them before. (0 number facts) Have the children write the answers to the number facts.

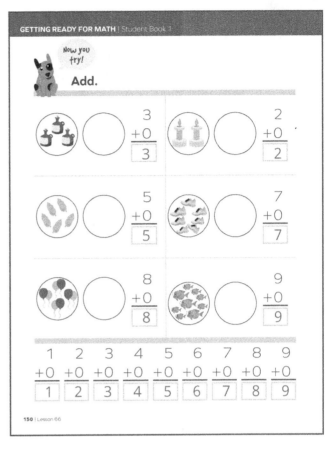

4. Turn to page 151. Read the directions at the top of the page and have the students write the answers. Read the directions at the middle of the page. Have the students read the number symbols and the number words. Be sure the children write the number symbols in the box and the number words on the line.

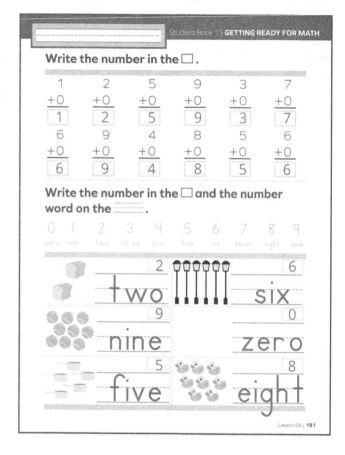

LESSON 67

MATERIALS NEEDED

- pencils
- set of 9 cards with numbers written on them (from Lesson 30)
- set of 9 cards with pictures (from Lesson 32)

Objectives:

1. To write the number words.
2. To write the number symbols in order.
3. To match number symbols and words.

Teaching Pages 152 and 153:

1. Turn to page 152. Have the students read the number symbols and the number words at the top of the page. Remind them that they have learned a new number value *0-zero* and that it comes before *one (1)* in number order. Read the directions aloud. Be sure the children understand that the number *symbol* is written after the number *word* and the number *word* is written after the number *symbol*. Remind the children to use good posture, to hold their pencils correctly, and to follow the procedures they have learned to form their letters.

2. Turn to page 153. Read the directions at the top of the page and have the students match number symbol to number word by drawing a line. Read the directions at the bottom of the page. Ask the children if the numbers in the first column are in correct number order. (no) Tell them to unscramble the number symbols and write them in the correct order.

3. Reintroduce the set of cards with numbers and pictures used in Lessons 30 and 32. Play several games of concentration with the students. Place the cards face down and take turns finding a match. Unmatched cards must be put back down exactly where they were picked up. The student with the most matches wins the game.

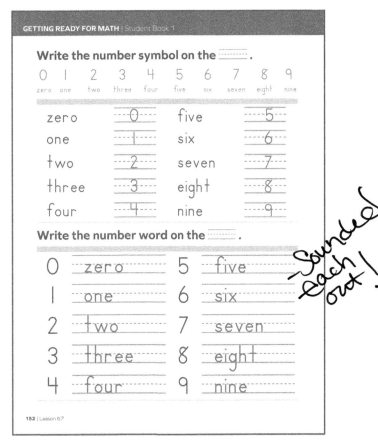

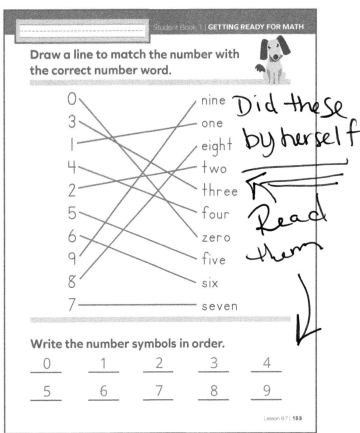

Sounded each out!

Did these by herself

Read them

LESSON 68

MATERIALS NEEDED

- pencils
- paper
- crayons—colors through orange

Objectives:

1. To write number symbols as number words.

2. To learn to follow directions.

Teaching Pages 154 and 155:

1. Turn to page 154. Read the title of the page. Have the children point to the first set and count the blocks. Then point to the number words and read them. Emphasize that the class is counting with number words. Give each student a piece of paper. Dictate the number words (one, two, three, four, five) to the students and have them write them on paper.

2. Introduce the game of "Sam says ...!" Tell the students that you will give them instructions but they should only follow them if you state: "Sam says ..." Give the students instructions such as, "Sam says stand up," "Sam says turn to your right," "Sam says turn to your left," "*Sit down*." If the students sit down, explain to them that they did not hear "Sam says ..." and so they should not have sat down. The children should have some fun with this game. Now have them look at page 155. Review the numbers at the top of the page, the colors on the side, and the shapes at the bottom. Tell the children you will give them directions but they should only follow them if "Sam says ..." Be sure the students have time to complete each instruction before going on to the next one. Say: "Sam says color the *big square* green. Sam says write the number *2* in front of the number *3*. Sam says write the number *one* after the *zero*. Color the *little square* blue. Sam says write the number word *six*

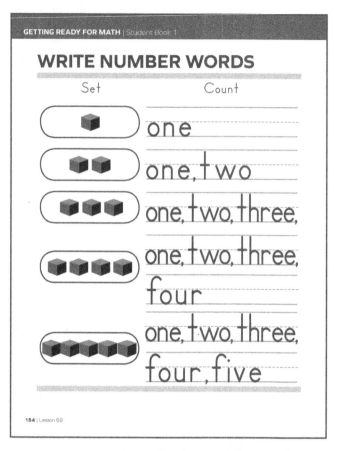

WRITE NUMBER WORDS

Set	Count
■	one
■■	one, two
■■■	one, two, three,
■■■■	one, two, three, four
■■■■	one, two, three, four, five

154 | Lesson 68

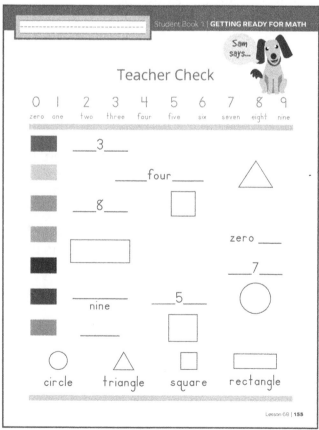

Student Book 1 | **GETTING READY FOR MATH**

Sam says...

Teacher Check

0	1	2	3	4	5	6	7	8	9
zero	one	two	three	four	five	six	seven	eight	nine

___3___

_____four_____

__8__

zero ___

__7__

nine   __5__

circle   triangle   square   rectangle

Lesson 68 | **155**

above the number word *nine*. <u>Write the number word *five* after the number word *four*.</u>" Continue in this manner until the page is completed. Give the instructions slowly to give the children an opportunity to be successful and enjoy the game.

She Loved the game and incorporating it into School work.

LESSON 69

MATERIALS NEEDED

- pencils
- scissors
- paper suitable for folding—$8\frac{1}{2}$ inches square—in color if possible

Objectives:

1. To write the number words to five.

2. To visualize and estimate shapes.

Teaching Pages 156 and 157:

1. Turn to pages 156 and 157. Read the directions aloud. Ask the class to count the illustrations aloud (the first one is zero). Tell them to write the number symbol (0) on the first line and the number word (zero) on the second line. Have the children complete pages 156 and 157 in this manner. Tell them to write neatly and use the correct procedures.

2. Make a triangle puzzle with the students using the paper square. Colored paper would make the puzzle more attractive. Ask the students to describe a triangle. Ask them if they can make two triangles out of the piece of paper. Tell them they must use the whole piece of paper for the two triangles. Let them spend some time visualizing how this can be done. When they are ready, have them cut the paper into the two triangles. Explain to them that this is a puzzle and they must put the puzzle pieces together again. Ask them if they can make two more triangles out of one (or both) of the puzzle pieces. Have them cut the pieces and then put the puzzle together again. Explain that a triangle may be many shapes but it must have three sides. Continue the division of pieces as long as the students are able to put the puzzle together again. Ask them to estimate how many triangles they think could be made from the original piece of paper. Similar exercises may be used for squares and rectangles to reinforce student recognition of flat shapes.

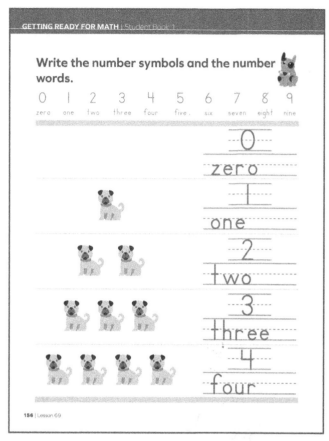

Write the number symbols and the number words.

0 1 2 3 4 5 6 7 8 9
zero one two three four five six seven eight nine

0
zero
1
one
2
two
3
three
4
four

156 | Lesson 69

Student Book 1 | GETTING READY FOR MATH

0 1 2 3 4 5 6 7 8 9
zero one two three four five six seven eight nine

5
five
6
six
7
seven
8
eight
9
nine

Lesson 69 | 157

LESSON 70

MATERIALS NEEDED

- pencils
- paper
- objects for counting
- fact cards for 0's, 1's, 2's

Objectives:

1. To use fact cards for 0's, 1's, 2's.

2. To write the number words to nine.

3. To learn number order.

4. To recognize colors and shapes.

Teaching Pages 158 and 159:

1. Review the fact cards for *0's*, *1's*, and *2's*. Always begin fact card time with the facts being presented in order and always allow the students to have objects for counting when necessary. If the students know the facts in order and do not require objects for counting, scramble the fact cards and present them in any order.

2. Turn to page 158. Read the directions aloud. Have the children point to the first set and count the planes. Then point to the number words and read them aloud. Tell them to write the number symbol and the number word. Complete the page in this manner.

3. Turn to page 159. Ask the students to read the number symbols and the number words in the two columns. Then review number order in this way. Point to the first column and have them say with you, "This is the first number (6), this is the second number (3)" and so on down the list of numbers. If children become confused, use the cards with the numbers *1–9* written on them. Take the number *6* and say, "This is the first number we have taken." Ask them to name the next number (3), take it from the group and say, "This is the second number we have taken" and so on to zero. Read

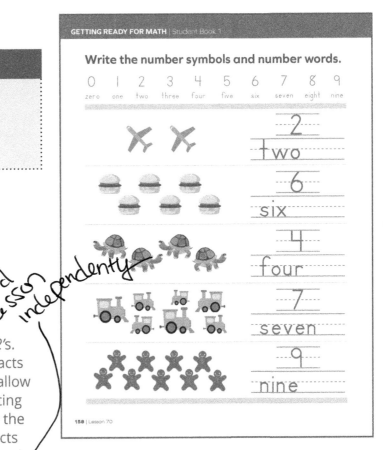

did Lesson independently

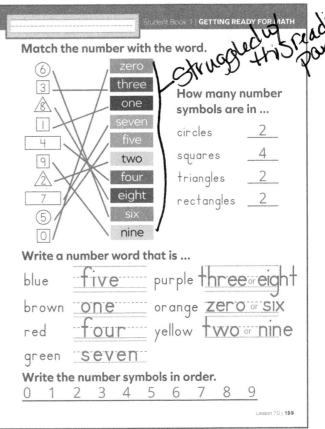

Struggled w/ this reading Part

the directions to page 159, and let the children complete the first part of the exercise. Read the directions for number symbols and directions for number words. Ask them to identify the shapes and colors on the page. Have them complete these exercises.

MATH KINDERGARTEN

Lessons 71–80

LESSON 71

MATERIALS NEEDED

- pencils
- paper
- objects for counting
- fact cards for 0's, 1's, 2's
- new set of fact cards (3 + 0, 3 + 1, 3 + 2, 3 + 3, 3 + 4, 3 + 5, 3 + 6)

Objectives:

1. To use fact cards for 0's, 1's, 2's, 3's.

2. To write the number words to nine.

3. To write number facts.

Teaching Pages 160 and 161:

1. Review the fact cards for *0's*, *1's*, and *2's*. Place the group of objects so that the students can reach them. Show the students the first fact card for *3's*. (3 + 0) Have the students make a set of three objects. Ask them what the card tells them to add to the set of *3*. (zero, nothing) Ask them what the answer is to *3 + 0*. (3) Proceed in this manner until all fact cards for *3's* have been used. Go through the fact cards a second time and have the students look again at the sets they have made.

2. Give the students pencil and paper. Dictate the following problems (number facts) including answers and have the children write them on paper. (Example: Three plus two equals five.) Be sure the students use the plus (add) sign and draw the line between the problem and the answer.
    Dictate:

3	2	0	2	3	1
+ 2	+ 4	+ 1	+ 5	+ 0	+ 2
5	6	1	7	3	3

3. Turn to page 160. Read the directions and have the children read the number words at the top of the page. Tell the children to point to the set of bears and count aloud. (1-2-3-4-5-6) Have them read the number words. Ask them which words are missing. Tell them to write the missing words on the lines.

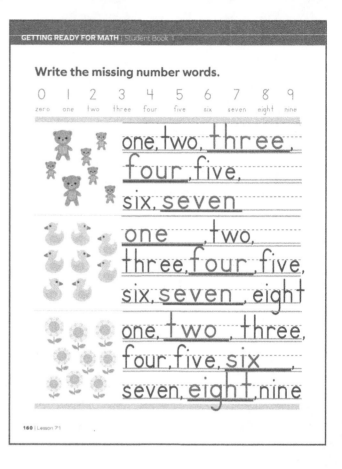

4. Turn to page 161. Read the directions to the children. Have them complete the page independently.

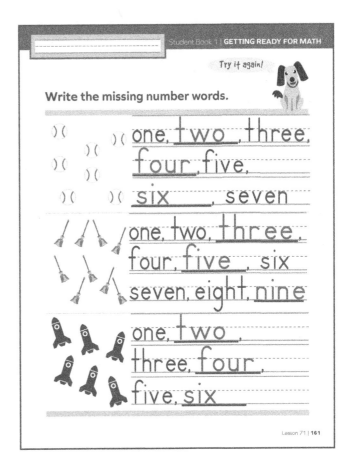

LESSON 72

MATERIALS NEEDED

- pencils
- objects for counting

Objectives:

1. To write the number words to nine.

2. To write number facts.

Teaching Pages 162 and 163:

1. Turn to page 162. Have the students read the number words at the top of the page and ask if they are in number order. Discuss number order *1-2-3*, etc. Tell the children that they should write the number words in order on the lines. Point to the next exercise and ask the children what these are. (number facts for zero) Have them complete this exercise. Read the directions for the last exercise and have the students complete the page.

2. Turn to page 163. Place the objects for counting within reach of the students. Read the directions at the top of the page. Encourage the students to complete the exercise without using the objects for counting if they are able. Some students may need the objects for some facts but not for others.

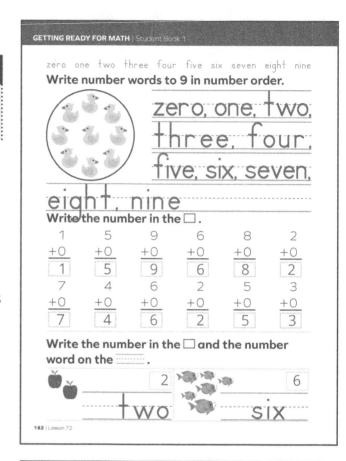

LESSON 73

MATERIALS NEEDED

- pencils
- objects for counting
- fact cards for 0's, 1's, 2's, 3's
- new sets of fact cards for 4's and 5's (4 + 0, 4 + 1, 4 + 2, 4 + 3, 4 + 4, 4 + 5) (5 + 0, 5 + 1, 5 + 2, 5 + 3, 5 + 4)

Objectives:

1. To use fact cards for 0's through 5's.

2. To add number words to five horizontally.

Teaching Pages 164 and 165:

1. Review the fact cards for 0's, 1's, 2's, 3's. Have the students use the objects for counting while the fact cards for 4's and 5's are being introduced. Go through the sets several times.

2. Turn to page 164. Read the title of the page and have the children point to the first row. Read aloud the statement under the first set of blocks. As you read, have the children point to the blocks. Tell the children to read the number words and the horizontal number facts aloud. Ask, "How many objects are there when you add one plus one?" Have the children point to the number word two. Read the words aloud, "One plus one equals two." Have the children read aloud until the entire page has been read.

3. Turn to page 165. Read the directions aloud. Tell the students to read the number words aloud. Allow the students to have their fact cards next to them. Ask the students to find the fact cards that correspond to the number word problems. (one + one = 1 + 1 =) Then have them write the answer on the line as a number word.

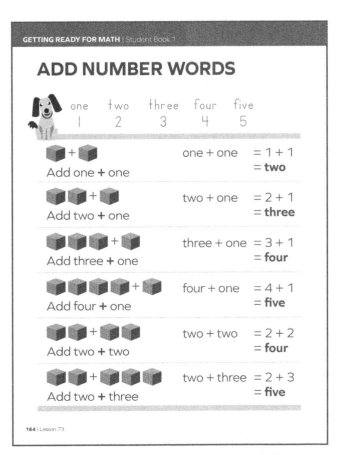

ADD NUMBER WORDS

one	two	three	four	five
1	2	3	4	5

Add one + one   one + one = 1 + 1 = **two**

Add two + one   two + one = 2 + 1 = **three**

Add three + one   three + one = 3 + 1 = **four**

Add four + one   four + one = 4 + 1 = **five**

Add two + two   two + two = 2 + 2 = **four**

Add two + three   two + three = 2 + 3 = **five**

164 | Lesson 73

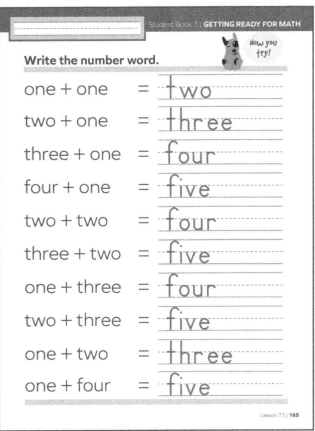

Student Book 1 | GETTING READY FOR MATH

Write the number word.

Now you try!

one + one	=	two
two + one	=	three
three + one	=	four
four + one	=	five
two + two	=	four
three + two	=	five
one + three	=	four
two + three	=	five
one + two	=	three
one + four	=	five

Lesson 73 | **165**

LESSON 74

MATERIALS NEEDED

- pencils
- objects for counting
- fact cards for 4's and 5's
- new sets of fact cards for 6's, 7's, 8's, and 9's
  (6 + 0, 6 + 1, 6 + 2, 6 + 3), (7 + 0, 7 + 1, 7 + 2),
  (8 + 0, 8 + 1), (9 + 0)

Objectives:

1. To use fact cards for 0's through 9's.

2. To add number words to nine horizontally.

Teaching Pages 166 and 167:

1. Review the fact cards for *4*'s and *5*'s and introduce the cards for *6*'s, *7*'s, *8*'s, and *9*'s. Use objects for counting to introduce the cards. Go over them several times.

2. Turn to page 166. Tell the children to point to the first set of blocks and read the number words. (Add four + two.) Point to the number symbols. (4 + 2) Ask the students if they know the answer to *4 + 2*. (6) Have the children read aloud until the entire page has been read. Use objects for counting, if necessary.

3. Turn to page 167. Read the directions aloud. Tell the students to read the number words aloud. Allow the students to have their fact cards next to them. Ask the students to find the fact cards that correspond to the number word problems. (one + two = 1 + 2 =) Tell them to write the answer on the line as a number word.

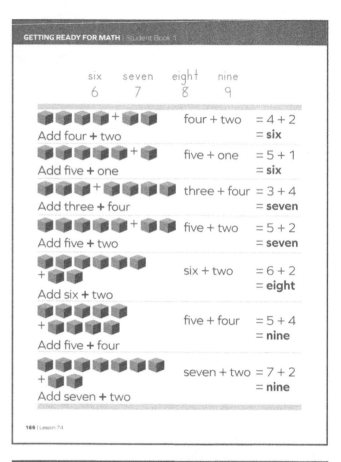

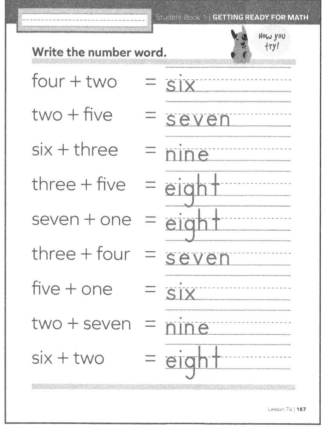

LESSON 75

MATERIALS NEEDED

- pencils
- paper
- objects for counting
- fact cards

Objectives:

1. To solve the problem of how many sets can be made from a group of objects.

2. To add number words to nine horizontally.

Teaching Page 168:

1. Place a group of five objects in front of the students. Ask them what it is. (a set of five objects) Ask the students if they can make two sets out of the set of five. Let the students respond *independently*. They may answer with sets of *2 + 3, 3 + 2, 1 + 4*, or *4 + 1*. Suppose a student responds with *2 + 3*. Have him write this as a fact on paper with the answer. Ask him to find the fact card. Next, ask him if there is another way to arrange his set of *2 + 3*. The response should be *3 + 2*. Ask him to write this as a fact on paper and ask him to locate this fact card. Put the five objects together in a group and ask him to find two more sets. Those children who found the sets of *2 + 3* and *3 + 2*, should now discover the sets of *1 + 4* and *4 + 1*. Ask them to write these facts on paper and find the fact cards. Keep the fact cards in front of the children so that they are aware of the different fact groups that produce an answer of *5*. (Some students may want to include the *0 + 5* and *5 + 0* facts.) Continue this type of problem solving using sets of *6, 7, 8, 9*. Be sure that the students discover all of the different combinations of facts that will produce the answers of *6, 7, 8,* and *9*.

2. Turn to page 168. Read the directions at the top of the page. Ask the students to answer each question by writing a number word.

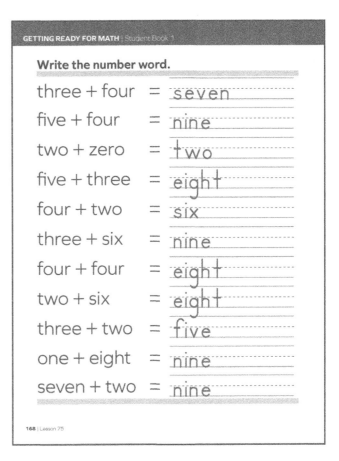

GETTING READY FOR MATH | Student Book 1

Write the number word.

three + four	=	seven
five + four	=	nine
two + zero	=	two
five + three	=	eight
four + two	=	six
three + six	=	nine
four + four	=	eight
two + six	=	eight
three + two	=	five
one + eight	=	nine
seven + two	=	nine

168 | Lesson 75

LESSON 76

MATERIALS NEEDED

- pencil
- objects for counting
- fact cards
- crayons—colors through orange

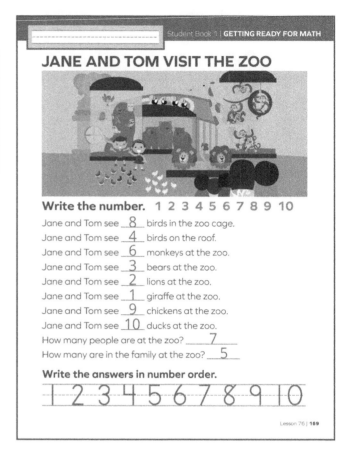

Objectives:

1. To learn the number 10.

2. To count objects to 10.

3. To review ordinal (order) numbers.

4. To learn more about facts to 9.

Teaching Pages 169 and 170:

1. Turn to page 169. Have the children look at the picture and read the title with them. Talk about visits to the zoo and zoo animals. Ask the children to identify the animals in the picture, to find Jane and Tom, and to identify the other visitors. (a family of five people) Point to the numbers and ask the children to count to nine. Then tell them that there is a new number to learn today. Write the number symbols on the board or on paper (0-1-2-3-4-5-6-7-8-9) so that the students can see and read them. Tell the students there are no more number symbols and so we continue counting using the same symbols. Write the number *10* (ten) on the board. Tell the students that this is the number that follows *9*. Ask the students to say the number *ten* aloud. Place ten objects in front of the students and have them count *1* through *10*. Return to page 169 and have the students point to the numbers and say them aloud. Read the directions and the questions aloud with the students, giving them time to write the answers on the lines. Then have them write the numbers in number order.

2. When the students have completed this exercise, ask them if there are any numbers missing. (No) Review the order (ordinal) numbers with the students. (first, second, third, and so on through tenth)

3. Then point to different animals at the zoo and ask if they are the first, second, third, and so on in their group.

4. Turn to page 170. Read the directions and tell the children to complete the page independently. Students may have fact cards and objects for counting if necessary. When the students have completed the page, tell them to follow these instructions. Find three different facts that have an answer of *5* and circle them with a *blue* crayon. Find three different facts that have an answer of *6* and circle them with a *green* crayon. Find three different facts that have an answer of 7 and circle them with a *purple* crayon. Find three different facts that have an answer of *8* and circle them with an orange crayon. Find three different facts that have an answer of *9* and circle them with a *red* crayon.

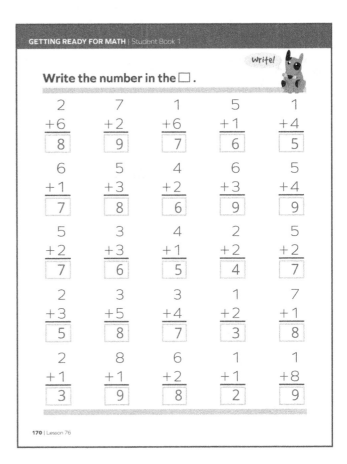

GETTING READY FOR MATH | Student Book 1

Write the number in the □ . write!

2	7	1	5	1
+6	+2	+6	+1	+4
8	9	7	6	5
6	5	4	6	5
+1	+3	+2	+3	+4
7	8	6	9	9
5	3	4	2	5
+2	+3	+1	+2	+2
7	6	5	4	7
2	3	3	1	7
+3	+5	+4	+2	+1
5	8	7	3	8
2	8	6	1	1
+1	+1	+2	+1	+8
3	9	8	2	9

170 | Lesson 76

LESSON 77

MATERIALS NEEDED

- pencils
- paper
- objects
- fact cards

Objectives:

1. To learn the numbers 11 and 12.

2. To count to 12.

3. To practice facts to 9 (horizontally).

Teaching Pages 171 and 172:

1. Turn to page 171. Read the title of the page and the directions with the children. Tell them to write the answers to the number facts. Then, have them write the number words on the blanks below the number symbols. When they have completed this exercise, place the objects so they are in reach of the children. Ask them to take objects from the group and count to *9* (0-1-2-3-4-5-6-7-8-9). Remind them that they have learned the next number and ask them what that is. (10) Go on to introduce the numbers *11* and *12* to them. Write the number symbols on paper or on the board for the children to see. Dictate the numbers from *0* through *12* and have the students write the number symbols on the bottom line on page 171. Ask the students to say the names as they write the number symbols.

2. Turn to page 172. Read the directions. Explain to the children that these number facts are written in a different direction (horizontally). Ask them if that changes the answers to the facts. Students may need to write some of the facts on paper in a similar manner to their fact cards (vertically). They may use objects for counting to understand that the fact answers are the same. Have them complete the page independently.

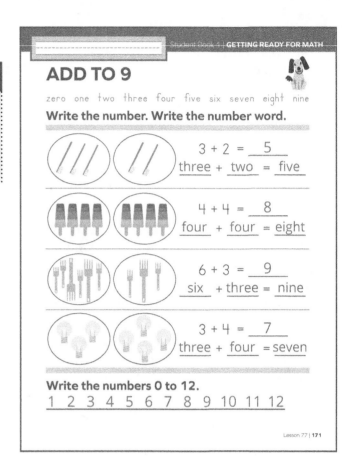

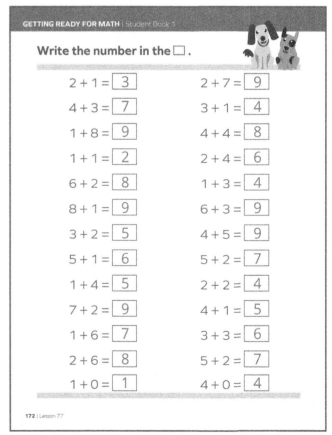

LESSON 78

MATERIALS NEEDED

- pencil
- objects for counting
- fact cards

Objectives:

1. To learn number facts vertically and horizontally.

2. To learn number facts written as words.

3. To write number words correctly.

Teaching Pages 173 and 174:

1. Review the fact cards with the students. Identify those facts that the students have mastered. (This may vary widely among students and must be worked with on an individual basis.) Congratulate the students for the facts that they have mastered, no matter how few. Set aside the mastered fact cards and spend a short time reviewing the remaining cards.

2. Turn to page 173. Read the directions and have the students complete the exercises. Encourage them to use proper posture and to hold their pencils correctly.

3. Turn to page 174. Read the directions to the first exercise and tell the students to write the words.

4. Read the second set of directions and have the students complete that exercise. Students should now understand that number facts may be written either vertically or horizontally. Allow them to use fact cards and objects only for those facts they have demonstrated that they have not mastered.

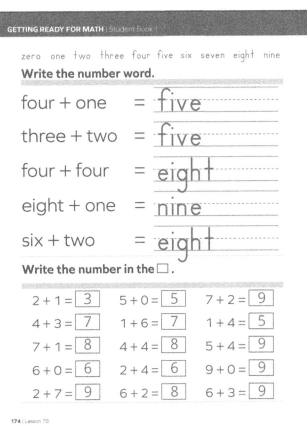

LESSON 79

MATERIALS NEEDED

- pencil
- objects for counting
- fact cards
- crayons—colors through orange

Objectives:

1. To learn number facts written horizontally in number symbols and number words.

2. To correctly identify colors through orange.

3. To write missing numbers through 12.

4. To tell ordinal (order) numbers and shapes.

5. To write the number word for before and after.

Teaching Pages 175, 176, and 177:

1. Turn to pages 175, 176, and 177. Read each set of directions and have the students complete the exercise before going on to the next set of directions. On workbook page 177, use the following instructions to complete the exercise *Tell the order numbers.* "Use your *blue* crayon to draw a *circle* around the *third* rose." "Use your *brown* crayon to draw a *square* around the *ninth* rose." "Use your *green* crayon to draw a *triangle* around the *first* rose." "Use your *purple* crayon to draw a *rectangle* around the *seventh* rose."

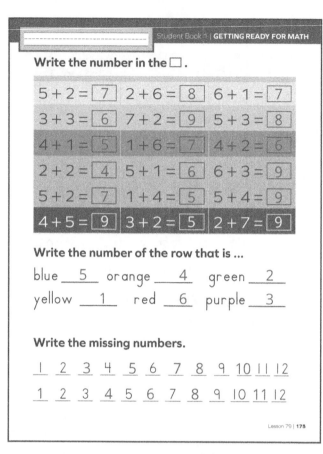

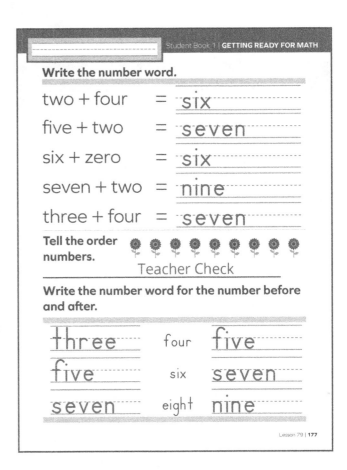

Write the number word.

two + four   = six

five + two   = seven

six + zero   = six

seven + two = nine

three + four = seven

Tell the order numbers.

Teacher Check

Write the number word for the number before and after.

three	four	five
five	six	seven
seven	eight	nine

Lesson 79 | **177**

161

LESSON 80

MATERIALS NEEDED

- pencil
- objects for counting
- fact cards
- crayons—colors through orange

Objectives:

1. To learn number facts written horizontally in number symbols and number words.

2. To correctly identify colors through orange.

3. To write missing numbers through 12.

4. To tell ordinal (order) numbers and shapes.

5. To write the number word for before and after.

Teaching Pages 178, 179, and 180:

1. Turn to pages 178, 179, and 180. Read each set of directions, and have the students complete the exercise before going on to the next set of directions. On workbook page 180, use the following instructions to complete the exercise: *Tell the order numbers*. "Use your *orange* crayon to draw a *square* around the *fourth* house." "Use your *yellow* crayon to draw a *triangle* around the *eighth* house." "Use your *brown* crayon to draw a *rectangle* around the *first* house." "Use your *purple* crayon to draw a *circle* around the *fifth* house."

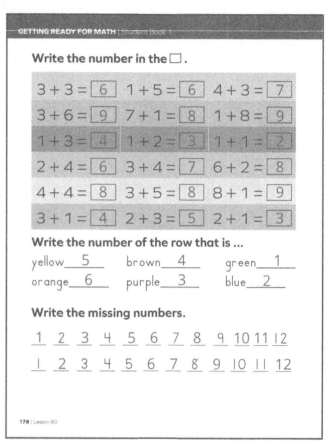

MATH KINDERGARTEN

Lessons 81–90

LESSON 81

MATERIALS NEEDED

- pencil
- objects for counting

Objectives:

1. To subtract one object from a set.

2. To subtract number facts to 5 vertically.

Teaching Pages 1, 2, and 3:

1. Turn to page 1. Point to the two dogs at the top of the page and ask the students if they know the dogs' names. Ask the students if they can read what Sam and Jip are saying. Give the children time to look through the workbooks, and then tell them to write their names on the line on page 1. Ask them what *score* means. Tell them that they should try to make good scores in this book. Allow time for them to complete the addition facts.

2. Explain to the children that this is an important day. Today they will learn their second math operation. It is called subtraction. Place five sets in front of the students of *5, 4, 3, 2,* and *1* objects.

3. Tell the students to *take away* one object from the set of *5* and ask how many objects are left. (4)

4. Tell the students that *take away* is called subtraction. Ask them to *take away* (subtract) one object from each of the remaining sets and tell how many are left.

5. Continue on page 2. Point to the word *subtract* and ask the students to say it aloud. Show the sets on page 2 to the students and tell them to point to the sets of objects that they have been working with. Ask them if the answers are the same. Point to the number facts between the sets and ask how they are different from the addition facts. (minus sign −) Ask the children to count the

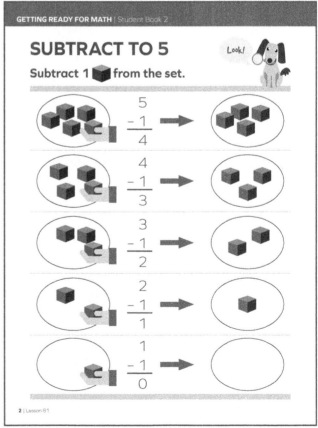

blocks in each set, and then say the number fact aloud. (five *minus* or *take away* one equals four) Some students will understand the expression *take away* better than *minus* or *subtract*. *Take away* is appropriate for beginning learners but the terms *minus* and *subtract* should also be used to build the students' vocabulary.

6. Turn to page 3. Place one object in front of the students. Ask them to read the first problem on page 3. (one *minus* or *take away* one) Have the students take one object away and then ask them how many are left. (none, nothing, zero) Ask them if they remember how to write nothing or zero. (0) Tell them to write the answer in the box. Continue in this manner to complete the page.

Student Book 2 | **GETTING READY FOR MATH**

You try it!

Write the number in the ☐ .

1	2	3	4	5	2
− 1	− 1	− 1	− 1	− 1	− 1
0	1	2	3	4	1

3	4	1	5	2	4
− 1	− 1	− 1	− 1	− 1	− 1
2	3	0	4	1	3

1	2	5	3	2	4
− 1	− 1	− 1	− 1	− 1	− 1
0	1	4	2	1	3

Lesson 81 | **3**

LESSON 82

MATERIALS NEEDED

- pencil
- objects for counting

Objectives:

1. To subtract two objects from a set.

2. To subtract number facts to 5 vertically.

Teaching Pages 4 and 5:

1. Place five sets in front of the students of *5*, *4*, *3*, *2*, and *1* objects. Tell the students to take away two objects from the set of 5 and ask how many objects are left. (3) Have them take away (subtract) two objects from each of the remaining sets and tell how many are left. Ask the students if they can take two objects from the set of one. (no)

2. Turn to page 4. Compare the sets on the page to the sets of objects that the students have been working with. Point out the number facts on the page and have the students identify the minus sign. Ask the students to read the number facts. (five *minus* or *take away* two equals three)

3. Turn to page 5. Place the objects in front of the students. Begin with the first fact. Have the students read the problem and then work it using the objects. When they have the correct answer, have them write the answer in the box. Complete the page in this manner.

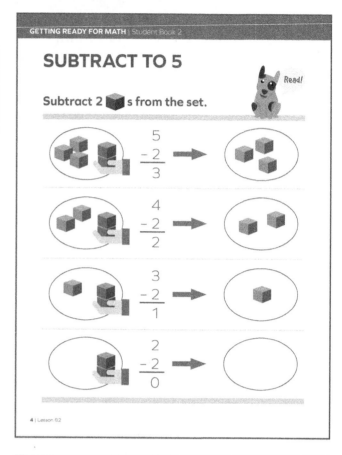

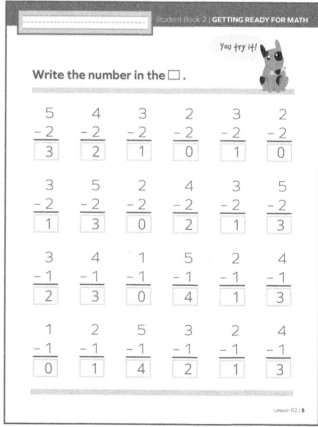

LESSON 83

MATERIALS NEEDED

- pencils
- objects for counting

Objectives:

1. To subtract three and four objects from a set.

2. To subtract number facts to 5 vertically.

Teaching Pages 6 and 7:

1. Place three sets in front of the students of *5*, *4*, and *3* objects. Tell the students to take away three objects from each set and ask how many objects are left. (2, 1, 0) Use the same procedure to take four objects from sets of *5* and *4*.

2. Turn to page 6. Compare the sets on the page to the sets of objects that the students have been working with. Point out the number facts on the page and have the students identify the minus sign. Ask the students to read the number facts aloud.

3. Turn to page 7. Have the children read the problem, solve the problem using the objects, and then write the answer below the number fact. Have them read the problem again after they have written the answer. (four minus three equals one)

4. When this page is completed, play a game with the students. Have them cover their eyes in some way so that they cannot see but have both hands free. Place a set of two objects in front of the students so they can touch them. Tell them you want to add one object to the set. Ask how many they would have if they added one object to the set. (3) Allow the children time to feel the two objects and think about their answers. Give them an object to add to the set only if necessary for counting. Place a group of four objects in front of the students and tell

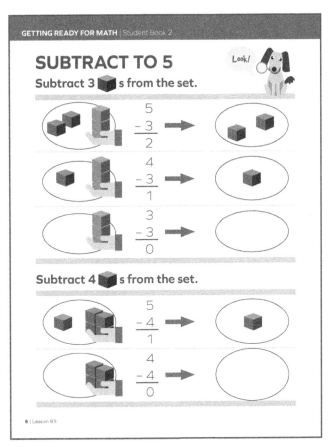

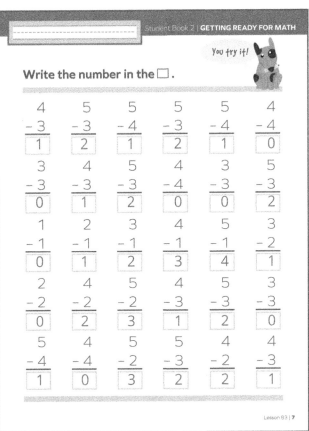

them you want to take one away. Ask how many they would have left. (3) Continue the add and take away game using different combinations of numbers only up to five objects. Develop the concept of the difference between addition and subtraction.

LESSON 84

MATERIALS NEEDED

- pencils
- objects for counting
- addition fact cards 0's through 9's
- crayons—colors through orange

Objectives:

1. To subtract number facts to 5 vertically.

2. To add number facts to 9 vertically.

Teaching Pages 8 and 9:

1. Turn to page 8. Read the title of the page and the instructions with the students. Give each student five objects to help in subtracting the number facts. Allow the children to complete the page independently.

2. Talk to the students about what it means to add to a number or take away from a number. Review the addition fact cards from 0's through 9's. Use objects for counting when necessary.

3. Turn to page 9. Ask the students to identify the pictures and then read *BE A STAR*. Tell them they can *BE A STAR* if they do well on this page. Ask them to read the signs and to say what the signs are telling them to do. Have them read the first problem. (six plus two) The students should complete the addition facts. They may use the colors shown on the page to color the stars. Be sure they color in the lines and in the same direction and can identify the colors as they use them.

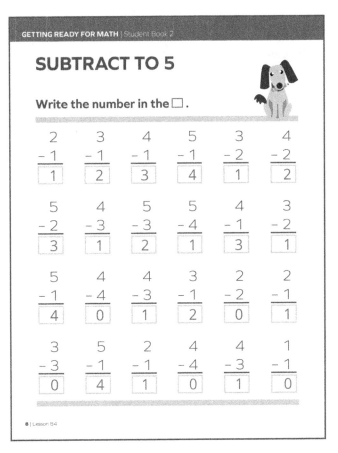

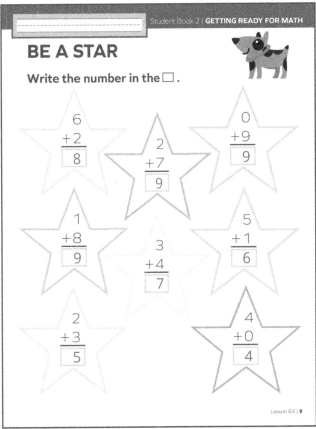

LESSON 85

MATERIALS NEEDED

- pencils
- objects for counting

Objectives:

1. To subtract one object from a set to 9.

2. To place number symbols and number words in number order.

Teaching Pages 10 and 11:

1. Place sets of *9, 8, 7,* and *6* objects in front of the students. Ask the students to take away (subtract) one object from each set and tell how many are left.

2. Turn to page 10. Read the directions on the page. Have the children count the blocks in the sets. Explain to them that the brown one is being taken away, and have them count the number left. Ask them to compare these sets to the sets of objects they were working with. Point to the number facts in the center, and have the students identify the minus sign. Ask the students to read the number facts aloud. (nine minus one equals eight)

3. Turn to page 11. Read the directions. Have the students use objects for counting to complete the first section and read the number facts when they are completed. Ask the students if the number symbols are in number order. Tell them to write them in the correct order. Have the students read the number words aloud.

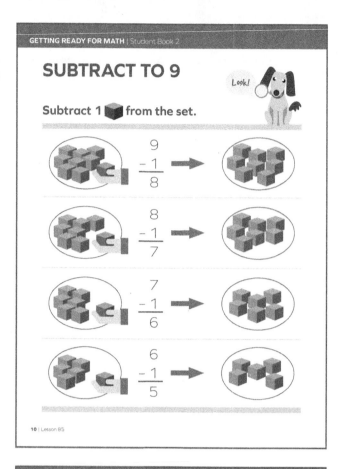

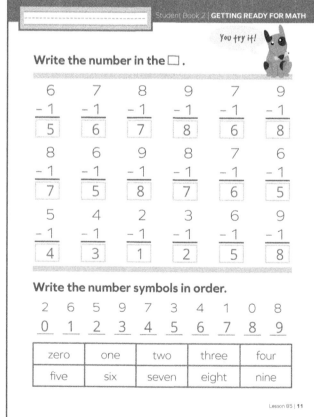

LESSON 86

MATERIALS NEEDED

- pencils
- objects for counting
- addition fact cards 0's through 9's
- ten pieces of cardboard, 2 inches by 3 inches in size
- cards with number pictures 1 through 9 (add one for zero) from Lesson 32
- paste or glue

Objectives:

1. To subtract two objects from a set to 9.

2. To find number facts for number words.

Teaching Pages 12 and 13:

1. Place sets of *9*, *8*, *7*, and *6* objects in front of the students. Ask the students to take away (subtract) two objects from each set and tell how many are left.

2. Turn to page 12. Read the directions on the page. Tell the children to count the blocks in the sets. Explain to them that the brown blocks are being taken away and have them count the number left. Ask them to compare these sets to the sets of objects they were working with. Point to the number facts in the center and have the students identify the minus sign. Ask the students to read the number facts. (nine minus two equals seven)

3. Turn to page 13. Read the directions. Allow the students to use objects for counting. Ask them to read the number facts when they are completed.

4. Have the students cut out the number words at the bottom of page 11, paste them to the pieces of cardboard, and then say them aloud. Mix the cards and tell the students to arrange them in number order.

5. Play a game of concentration using the number picture cards from Lesson 32 and the number word cards from this lesson.

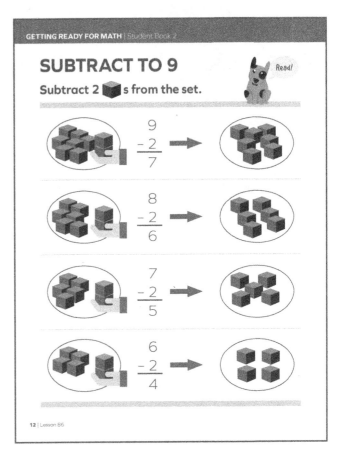

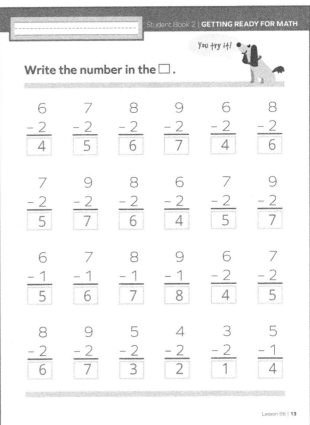

LESSON 87

MATERIALS NEEDED

- pencils
- objects for counting
- cards with number symbols 0 through 9 from Lesson 30
- number words zero through nine from Lesson 86

Objectives:

1. To subtract three objects from a set to 9.

2. To find the missing number.

3. To find the number that comes before and after.

4. To put numbers in number order.

Teaching Pages 14 and 15:

1. Place sets of *9*, *8*, *7*, and *6* objects in front of the students. Ask the students to take away (subtract) three objects from each set and tell how many are left.

2. Turn to page 14. Read the directions on the page. Tell the children to count the blocks in the sets. Explain to them that three blocks are being taken away and have them count the number left. Ask them to compare these sets to the sets of objects they were working with. Point to the number facts in the center and have the students identify the minus sign. Ask the students to read the number facts. (nine minus three equals six)

3. Turn to page 15, and have the students complete the page using objects for counting.

4. Use the number symbol and number word cards to play a *before* and *after* or *missing number* game. Place two number symbol cards (3 and 5) in front of the students. Ask them to find the missing number word card and put it in the correct place. Select a number word card (seven) and ask the students to select the number symbol cards

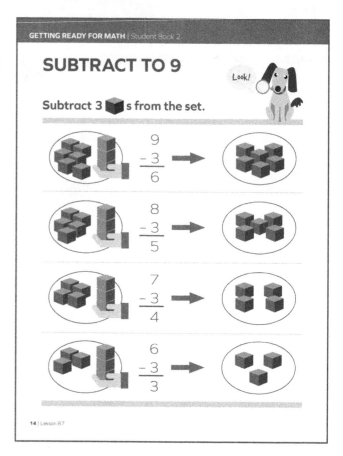

that come before and after and place them in the correct position. Place two cards in front of the students and have them find the number between. Continue with this exercise for a short period. Before completing the exercise, have the students place the number symbols and number words in number order.

LESSON 88

MATERIALS NEEDED

- pencils
- objects for counting
- addition fact cards 0 through 9
- subtraction fact cards for 1's, 2's, 3's (1 – 0, 1 – 1) (2 – 0, 2 – 1, 2 – 2) (3 – 0, 3 – 1, 3 – 2, 3 – 3)

Objectives:

1. To subtract four and five objects from a set to 9.

2. To review addition fact cards to 9.

3. To learn about subtraction fact cards for 1's, 2's, and 3's.

Teaching Pages 16 and 17:

1. Place sets of *9, 8, 7,* and *6* objects in front of the students. Ask the students to take away (subtract) four and five objects from each set and tell how many are left.

2. Turn to page 16. Read the directions on the page. Have the children count the blocks in the sets. Explain to them that four blocks are being taken away and have them count the number left. Ask them to compare these sets to the sets of objects they were working with. Point to the number facts in the center and have the students identify the minus sign. Ask the students to read the number facts. (nine minus four equals five)

3. Turn to page 17, and tell the students to complete the page using objects for counting.

4. Place all of the addition fact cards *0's* through *9's* in separate piles grouped in *0's* through *9's*. Explain to the children that addition was the first math operation that they learned and these are the addition fact cards. Let them look through them. Point out the addition sign. Tell them that it is important they know their facts and that is

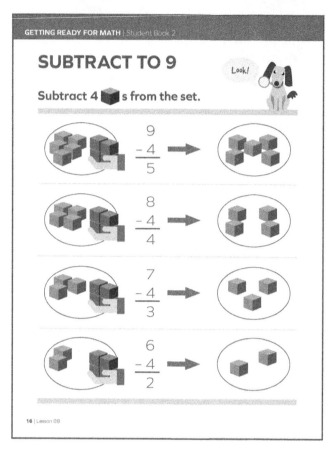

GETTING READY FOR MATH | Student Book 2

SUBTRACT TO 9

Look!

Subtract 4 ■s from the set.

$$\begin{array}{r} 9 \\ -4 \\ \hline 5 \end{array}$$

$$\begin{array}{r} 8 \\ -4 \\ \hline 4 \end{array}$$

$$\begin{array}{r} 7 \\ -4 \\ \hline 3 \end{array}$$

$$\begin{array}{r} 6 \\ -4 \\ \hline 2 \end{array}$$

16 | Lesson 88

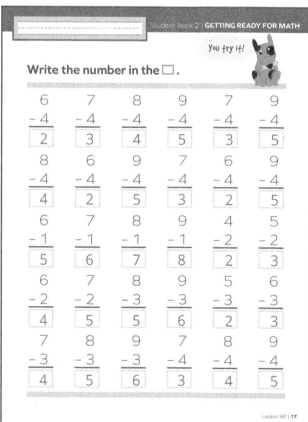

Student Book 2 | **GETTING READY FOR MATH**

You try it!

Write the number in the □.

6	7	8	9	7	9
– 4	– 4	– 4	– 4	– 4	– 4
2	3	4	5	3	5
8	6	9	7	6	9
– 4	– 4	– 4	– 4	– 4	– 4
4	2	5	3	2	5
6	7	8	9	4	5
– 1	– 1	– 1	– 1	– 2	– 2
5	6	7	8	2	3
6	7	8	9	5	6
– 2	– 2	– 3	– 3	– 3	– 3
4	5	5	6	2	3
7	8	9	7	8	9
– 3	– 3	– 3	– 4	– 4	– 4
4	5	6	3	4	5

Lesson 88 | **17**

why we have fact cards. Set these aside and say, "These are the addition fact cards." Ask them to name the second math operation that they have learned (subtraction). Show them the fact card for *1 – 1* and point out the minus sign. Have them illustrate the fact card using objects for counting.

5. Go on to introduce the subtraction fact cards for *2*'s and *3*'s. When finished, place these cards in separate piles and say, "These are the subtraction fact cards."

LESSON 89

MATERIALS NEEDED

- pencils
- crayons through orange
- number symbol cards 1 through 9
- new number symbol cards for 10's, 11's, and 12's

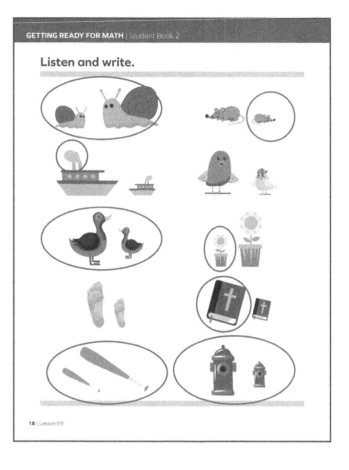

Listen and write.

18 | Lesson 89

Objectives:

1. To review right, left, up, down, over, under, below, above, big, little.

2. To write number symbols in order through 12.

Teaching Pages 18 and 19:

1. Play the game of *"Sam Says!"* using directions right and left, up and down, over and under, above and below, big and little. *"Sam says* put your *right* hand behind your back. *Sam says* put your *left* foot *up*; put your *left* foot *down*." Of course, no one follows a direction unless *"Sam says."* Continue this game to practice following the directions shown in the objectives.

2. Turn to page 18. Have the students identify all the objects on the page. Be sure they understand what each one is. Tell them to carefully follow the directions that you are going to give to them. "Put your finger on the paper and move it *down* to the *red fire hydrants*. Circle them with your *green* crayon. Move your finger *up* the page to the *little* yellow flower with the *green* stem. Circle it with a *brown* crayon. Find the objects *below* the two feet. Circle them with a *blue* crayon. Find the picture of the snails that is *over* the picture of the boats. Circle them with a *red* crayon. Find the two Bibles. Circle the one on the *left* with a *yellow* crayon. Find the two mice. Circle the one on the *right* with a *green* crayon. Find the ducks that are *under* the boats. Circle them with an *orange* crayon. Find the smoke that is above the *big* boat. Circle it with a *purple* crayon."

3. Place a group of twelve objects in front of the students. Ask them if they remember how to count to *twelve*. Review Lesson 77 if necessary. Tell the students to take one object at a time until they count to 12. Mix the cards with numbers (1–12) and have the students put them in number order.

4. Turn to page 19. Have the students match the number symbols with the number pictures. Tell them to write the number symbols in number order at the bottom of the page.

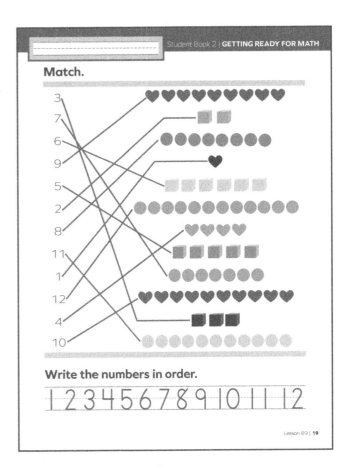

LESSON 90

MATERIALS NEEDED

- pencils
- a group of five empty metal or plastic containers of varying size—half cup to two cups
- a group of small- to medium-sized objects
- objects for counting
- construction paper
- scissors

Objectives:

1. To review big and little.

2. To estimate how many.

3. To review addition facts through 9.

Teaching Pages 20 and 21:

1. Place the containers in front of the students and ask them to arrange them in order from smallest to largest (little to big). Show the group of objects to the students. Ask them to select the number of objects it would take for them to fill the first (smallest) container. Tell them to fill the container and to find out how close they were to being right. Ask them if they will need more objects or less objects to fill the next container. Ask them to show you how many more or less. Have them fill the second container with the objects from the first container and as many more as they estimated. Go on with the exercise until all containers have been used. Determine whether the students' ability to estimate improves by the time they have filled the final (biggest) container. Do they realize they will need more objects as the containers become larger?

2. Turn to page 21. Have the students complete the page of addition facts. Let them use objects for counting if needed.

3. Turn to page 20. Point to the empty jar and the piece of candy at the bottom of the page. Ask the students how many pieces of

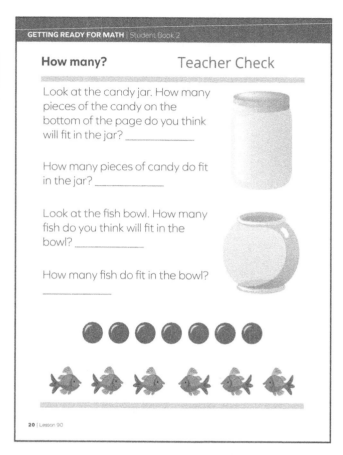

GETTING READY FOR MATH | Student Book 2

How many?   Teacher Check

Look at the candy jar. How many pieces of the candy on the bottom of the page do you think will fit in the jar? _____

How many pieces of candy do fit in the jar? _____

Look at the fish bowl. How many fish do you think will fit in the bowl? _____

How many fish do fit in the bowl? _____

20 | Lesson 90

Student Book 2 | GETTING READY FOR MATH

Write the number in the ☐ .

4 +3 = 7

6 +1 = 7

5 +2 = 7

3 +1 = 4

6 +2 = 8

5 +4 = 9

2 +3 = 5

3 +5 = 8

2 +7 = 9

3 +4 = 7

2 +2 = 4

Lesson 90 | 21

candy they would need to fill the jar. Follow the same directions for the fish bowl and the fish. Help the children cut out the pieces of candy at the bottom of the page. (They do not need to be exact in their cutting.) Use the construction paper to cut out more pieces if necessary. Glue the pieces to the inside of the jar on page 20 until it is full. Then, have the children count the number of pieces and compare this number to their estimation. Follow the same procedure with the fish bowl and fish.

MATH KINDERGARTEN

Lessons 91–100

LESSON 91

MATERIALS NEEDED

• pencils
• objects for counting
• addition fact cards through 9
• subtraction fact cards for 1's, 2's, and 3's
• subtraction fact cards for 4's (4 – 1, 4 – 2, 4 – 3, 4 – 4) and 5's (5 – 1, 5 – 2, 5 – 3, 5 – 4, 5 – 5)

Objective:

To review addition and subtraction facts through 9.

Teaching Pages 22 and 23:

1. It is important for students to visualize or form a mental picture of the addition and subtraction facts. Take time to allow them to do this. Students who simply try to memorize the facts will become confused.

2. Have the students go through the *addition fact cards* in order. If they do not know an answer, make a set of objects for the first number and then ask them to visualize adding the second number. If they still have difficulty, allow them to count out the additional objects. Set aside those fact cards they do not know and work on them for a short time at the end of each day's lesson.

3. Turn to page 22. Read the directions and tell the students to complete the page. They may use fact cards or objects for counting where necessary.

4. Have the students go through the *subtraction fact cards* in order. If they do not know an answer, make a set of objects for the first number and then ask them to visualize subtracting the second number of objects. If they still have difficulty, allow them to take away the objects. Set aside those fact cards they do not know and work on them for a short time at the end of each day's lesson.

GETTING READY FOR MATH | Student Book 2

Write the number in the ☐ .

3	2	6	1	0	8
+1	+4	+2	+5	+2	+1
4	6	8	6	2	9
5	3	4	5	1	3
+2	+6	+4	+3	+2	+3
7	9	8	8	3	6
2	1	4	3	4	2
+3	+6	+2	+4	+5	+2
5	7	6	7	9	4
7	8	2	6	2	8
+1	+1	+5	+3	+7	+0
8	9	7	9	9	8
5	1	4	7	4	2
+2	+1	+5	+2	+1	+2
7	2	9	9	5	4

22 | Lesson 91

5. Turn to page 23. Read the directions. Point out the sign for these problems (minus sign) and talk about how it is different from the addition sign. The students should complete the page independently. They may use fact cards or objects for counting.

Student Book 2 | **GETTING READY FOR MATH**

You try it!

Write the number in the ☐.

6	7	8	9	6	7
− 1	− 1	− 1	− 1	− 2	− 2
5	6	7	8	4	5

8	9	6	7	8	9
− 2	− 2	− 3	− 3	− 3	− 3
6	7	3	4	5	6

6	7	8	9	2	3
− 4	− 4	− 4	− 4	− 1	− 1
2	3	4	5	1	2

4	5	3	4	5	4
− 1	− 1	− 2	− 3	− 2	− 3
3	4	1	1	3	1

5	5	9	9	8	8
− 3	− 4	− 5	− 6	− 5	− 4
2	1	4	3	3	4

Lesson 91 | **23**

LESSON 92

MATERIALS NEEDED

- pencils
- crayons through orange
- objects for counting

Objectives:

1. To identify shapes.

2. To practice addition and subtraction facts.

Teaching Pages 24, 25, and 26:

1. Turn to page 24. Have the students look at the picture and identify the different shapes. Be sure they understand the difference between the squares and rectangles. Talk about big and little shapes.

2. Read the first direction, and give the children time to color the different shapes. Remind them to stay in the lines and to color in one direction. Read the second direction with the children. Have them count *how many* and write the answer. Call attention to the number of circles and ask the children if they know an addition fact that would describe the number of circles. (2 + 1 = 3 or 1 + 2 = 3) See if the students can find different fact combinations for the squares, rectangles, and triangles. Have the children write one of the facts for each shape on the page.

3. Turn to page 25. Ask the students what kind of shapes they see on this page (rectangles). Tell them to point to each rectangle and say the name of the color. Ask them to find Jip and the red ball on the page. Tell them that Jip wants to find his ball but he must go between the rectangles and not across any of them to do this. Tell them to use their pencils to find a path for Jip to follow. Try to have them find more than one path.

FIND THE SHAPES!

Look at the picture.

Color the circles green.

Color the squares red.

Color the rectangles yellow.

Color the triangles purple.

Teacher Check

Write the answer.

How many circles?   ○   3

How many squares?   □   2

How many rectangles?   ▭   4

How many triangles?   △   5

Write an addition fact for how many ...

circles   _____ + _____ Teacher Check

squares   _____ + _____ = _____

rectangle   _____ + _____ = _____

triangles   _____ + _____ = _____

24 | Lesson 92

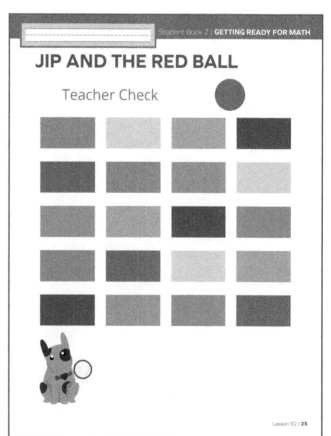

Student Book 2 | **GETTING READY FOR MATH**

JIP AND THE RED BALL

Teacher Check

Lesson 92 | **25**

4. Turn to page 26. Ask the children if they think this is one of the animals that went on Noah's Ark. Remind them of the story from Lesson 14. Ask them what kind of an animal it is. (camel) Read the problems aloud with the children. Be sure they read the addition and subtraction signs correctly. Tell them to complete the number facts and to use their crayons to color the camel.

LESSON 93

MATERIALS NEEDED

- pencils
- a piece of cardboard, 6 inches by 6 inches
- string or yarn
- scissors
- brass brad
- glue

Objectives:

1. To count with a number line.

2. To make a clock using a number line.

Teaching Pages 27, 28, and 29:

1. Turn to page 27. Have the children use each of the number lines to count out loud. Point to each number as they count. Call attention to the number line at the bottom of the page and read what Sam is saying.

2. Turn to pages 28 and 29. Use the directions on page 29 to make a clock. Use the brass brad to attach the hands to the center of the clock so the hands may move freely. Tell the children they will use this clock to tell time. *(Save clock made in this activity for later lessons.)*

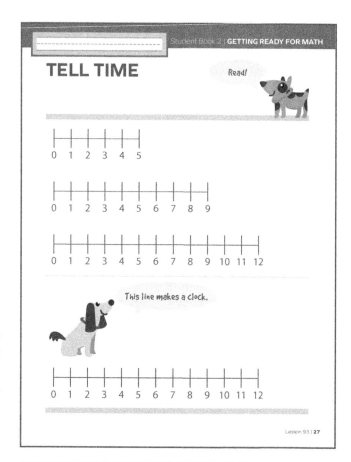

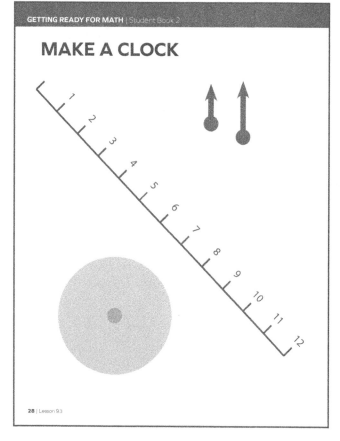

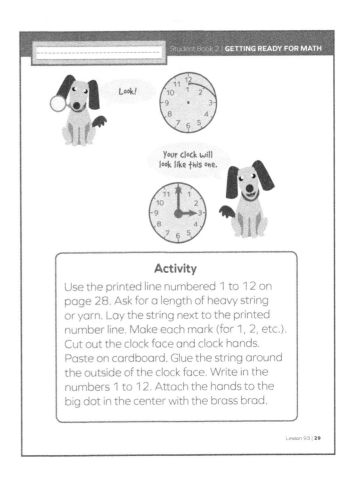

LESSON 94

MATERIALS NEEDED

• pencils
• clock made in Lesson 93

Objective:

To tell the hour on the clock.

Teaching Pages 30 and 31:

1. Turn to page 30. Read the title of the page. Read, "A clock has a face." Have the children point to the clock's face. Tell the children to point to the face on the clock they have made. State, "A clock has two hands—one long hand and one short hand." Tell the children to point to each hand on the clock they have made. Have the children identify the hands on the clock on page 30. State that the long hand is on the twelve and the short hand is on the number of the hour. (3) Have the children repeat the time "three o'clock" with you. Then have them turn the hands on their clocks so they show 3 o'clock. Have the children point to the first clock. Move the hands on their clocks to the same positions. Ask, "The long hand is on what number?" (twelve) "The short hand is on what number?" (one) "What time is it?" (one o'clock) Repeat this procedure for each of the clocks on page 30.

2. Turn to page 31. Read the directions out loud. Have the children point to the first clock on page 31. Emphasize that the short hand is on the number for the hour. Tell them to put the hands on their clocks so they are the same as the first clock. Tell them to read the time aloud and then write the number on the line. Have them complete the page in the same manner.

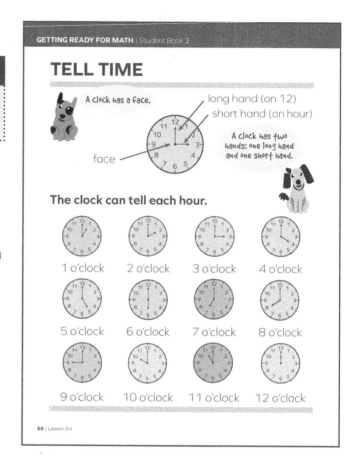

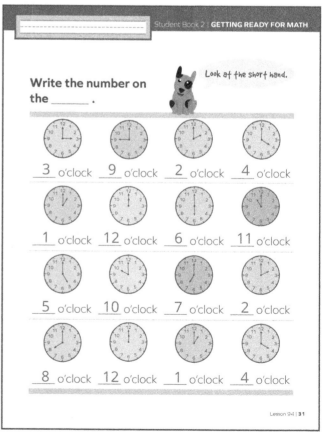

LESSON 95

MATERIALS NEEDED

- pencils
- number cards from Lessons 30 (symbols) and 86 (words)

Objective:

To practice writing number symbols and number words through 9.

Teaching Pages 32 and 33:

1. Review the instructions from Lesson 12 for proper posture and how to hold a pencil.

2. Turn to page 32. Ask the students to read each number symbol and trace it with their fingers. Have them write each of the number symbols six times. Tell them to work slowly and to be very neat.

3. Turn to page 33. Ask the students to read each number symbol and write each number symbol once next to the number symbol on the page. Have the students read the number words and write each number word once next to the number word on the page.

4. Use the number cards from Lessons 30 and 86 to play a game of concentration.

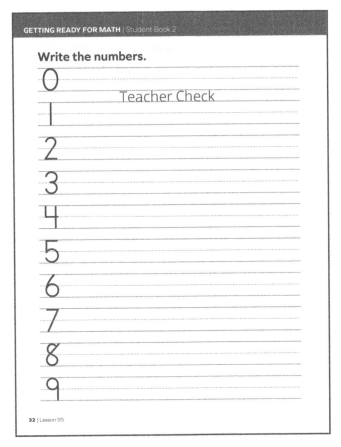

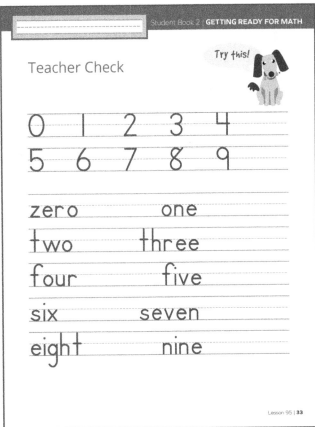

LESSON 96

MATERIALS NEEDED

- pencils
- objects for counting
- addition fact cards 0's through 9's
- subtraction fact cards 1's through 5's
- subtraction fact cards for 6's (6 – 1, 6 – 2, 6 – 3, 6 – 4, 6 – 5, 6 – 6), 7's (7 – 1, 7 – 2, 7 – 3, 7 – 4, 7 – 5, 7 – 6, 7 – 7), 8's (8 – 1, 8 – 2, 8 – 3, 8 – 4, 8 – 5, 8 – 6, 8 – 7, 8 – 8), and 9's (9 – 1, 9 – 2, 9 – 3, 9 – 4, 9 – 5, 9 – 6, 9 – 7, 9 – 8, 9 – 9)

Objective:

To understand addition and subtraction facts through 9 in number symbols and number words vertically and horizontally.

Teaching Pages 34 and 35:

1. Remember to lead the students toward visualizing the addition and subtraction facts. Students who simply try to memorize the facts do not understand the concept.

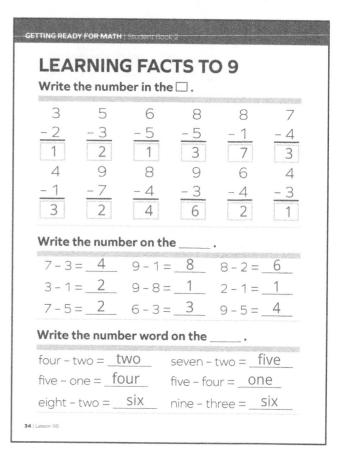

GETTING READY FOR MATH | Student Book 2

LEARNING FACTS TO 9

Write the number in the □.

3	5	6	8	8	7
– 2	– 3	– 5	– 5	– 1	– 4
1	2	1	3	7	3

4	9	8	9	6	4
– 1	– 7	– 4	– 3	– 4	– 3
3	2	4	6	2	1

Write the number on the _____ .

7 – 3 = __4__   9 – 1 = __8__   8 – 2 = __6__

3 – 1 = __2__   9 – 8 = __1__   2 – 1 = __1__

7 – 5 = __2__   6 – 3 = __3__   9 – 5 = __4__

Write the number word on the _____ .

four – two = __two__   seven – two = __five__

five – one = __four__   five – four = __one__

eight – two = __six__   nine – three = __six__

34 | Lesson 96

2. Have the students go through the subtraction fact cards for 6's, 7's, 8's, and 9's in order. Some of these facts will be new to the children. If they do not know an answer, make a set of objects for the first number and then ask them to visualize subtracting the second number of objects. If they still have difficulty, allow them to take away the objects. Set aside those fact cards that they do not know and work on them for a short time at the end of today's lesson.

3. Turn to page 34. Read the directions. Point out the sign for these problems (minus sign) and talk about how it is different from the addition sign. Point out the three sections of the page and have the students read aloud at least one problem from each section. Compare the vertical and horizontal problems, number symbol, and number word problems. Show the children that their answers will be the same no matter how the problem is written. They may use fact cards or objects for counting.

4. Turn to page 35. Read the directions. Point out the sign for these problems (addition sign) and talk about how it is different from the subtraction (minus) sign. Point out the three sections of the page and have the students read aloud at least one problem from each section. The students should complete the page independently. They may use fact cards or objects for counting where necessary.

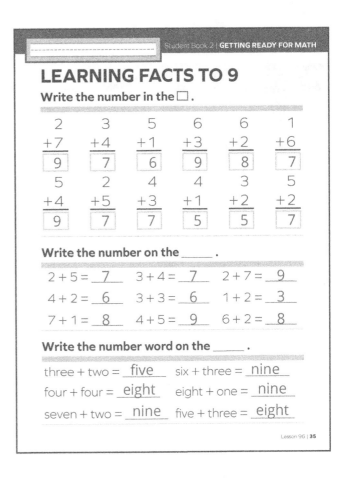

LESSON 97

MATERIALS NEEDED

- pencils
- crayons through orange
- black crayon

Objectives:

1. To write number facts.

2. To count ordinal (order) numbers.

3. To tell time to the hour.

4. To learn the new color black.

Teaching Pages 36 and 37:

1. Turn to pages 36 and 37. Ask the students to select the crayon as you say each color: red, yellow, green, blue, brown, purple, and orange. Introduce the new color black. Read the nursery rhyme about Old King Cole to the students:

   Old King Cole was a merry old soul
   and a merry old soul was he;
   He called for his pipe,
   and he called for his bowl,
   and he called for his fiddlers three.

2. Ask the students to find Old King Cole, the bowl, the pipe, and the fiddlers. Tell them to find the first, second, and third fiddler and the first, second, and third ant. Have them complete the facts on page 36.

3. Turn to page 37. Tell the children to look at page 36 and then write the facts that make 6. Have them circle the facts that make 7 with a green crayon and put an X on the facts that make 8 with an orange crayon. Have them write the facts that make 9. Ask them to find the clock and write what time it is.

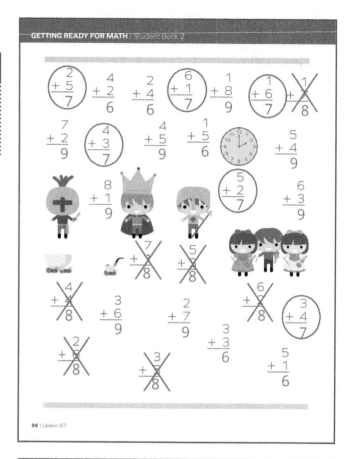

LESSON 98

MATERIALS NEEDED

- pencils

Objectives:

1. To write number facts.
2. To match number symbols to number words.
3. To match shapes.
4. To write numbers in number order.
5. To tell numbers before and after.

Teaching Pages 38, 39, and 40:

1. Turn to page 38. Have the students count the paint brushes in the sets at the top of the page. Ask them how the paint brushes in the sets relate to the numbers and the sign in the number facts. Tell them to write the answer to the number fact in the box. Tell the students to count the rockets in the first set (8) and write that as the first number of their problem. Have them count the number of rockets to be removed (2) and write the *2* below the *8*. Then have them count the number in the third set (6) and write the *6* as the answer to the number fact. Complete the page in the same manner.

2. Turn to page 39. Read the direction word with the children. Ask them to read the first number fact and ask them for the answer. Tell them to find the number word in the second column and match it with the number fact. When this is completed, have them name and match the shapes in the two columns. Ask them to identify the colors of the shapes. Read the direction *Write the problem*, and explain to them that you are going to dictate four number facts to them. They should write the number facts on the bottom of page 39. Carefully check the students for placement of numbers, use of the

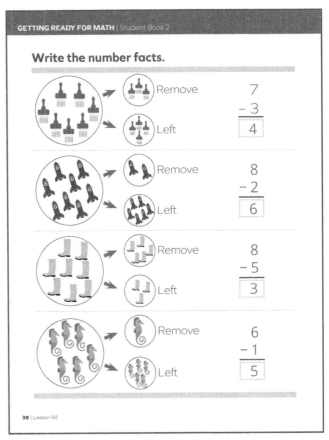

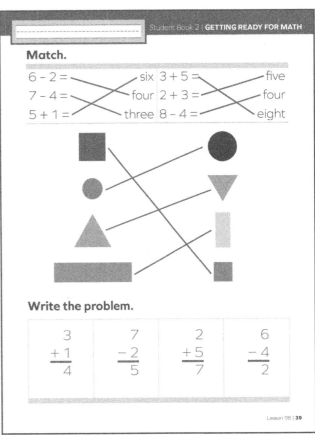

correct sign, and drawing a line between the problem and the answer.

3. Dictate:

Three plus one equals four.

$$\begin{array}{r} 3 \\ + 1 \\ \hline 4 \end{array}$$

Seven minus two equals five.

$$\begin{array}{r} 7 \\ - 2 \\ \hline 5 \end{array}$$

Two plus five equals seven.

$$\begin{array}{r} 2 \\ + 5 \\ \hline 7 \end{array}$$

Six minus four equals two.

$$\begin{array}{r} 6 \\ - 4 \\ \hline 2 \end{array}$$

4. Turn to page 40. Read the first set of directions, and have the children complete the section. Complete the remainder of the page, reading directions with the students as they are ready for the next section.

GETTING READY FOR MATH | Student Book 2

Write the number in the ☐.

$$\begin{array}{r} 3 \\ - 1 \\ \hline \boxed{2} \end{array} \quad \begin{array}{r} 7 \\ - 3 \\ \hline \boxed{4} \end{array} \quad \begin{array}{r} 9 \\ - 4 \\ \hline \boxed{5} \end{array} \quad \begin{array}{r} 2 \\ - 1 \\ \hline \boxed{1} \end{array} \quad \begin{array}{r} 8 \\ - 2 \\ \hline \boxed{6} \end{array} \quad \begin{array}{r} 9 \\ - 1 \\ \hline \boxed{8} \end{array}$$

Write the missing numbers.

0   1   2   3   4   5   6   7   8

Write the number before.

___2___ 3   ___5___ 6   ___3___ 4

___0___ 1   ___4___ 5   ___8___ 9

Write the number after.

2 ___3___   8 ___9___   4 ___5___

0 ___1___   3 ___4___   7 ___8___

LESSON 99

MATERIALS NEEDED

- pencils
- crayons through orange
- black crayon

Objectives:

1. To write number symbols in number order.

2. To write the signs for add and subtract.

3. To review right, left, above, below.

4. To solve number facts.

Teaching Pages 41, 42, and 43:

1. Turn to page 41. Section 1: Dictate the number symbols *0* through *12* to the students and have them write them on the blank lines at the top of the page. Ask the students if they have written the number symbols in number order (yes) and have them read them aloud. Section 2: Tell the children that you are going to dictate two numbers to them and they are to write the numbers in correct number order. Sometimes you may say them in the right order, sometimes you may not. Students may look at the numbers written in order for help. Dictate: *5-4* (4-5), *7-8* (7-8), *3-2* (2- 3), *2-1* (1-2), *7-6* (6-7), *8-9* (8-9). Section 3: Ask the students to write the symbol that tells them to add, to subtract. Section 4: Tell the students to look at the four facts. Ask them what symbol (+ or −) is missing. Tell them to write the symbol. Students may use manipulatives to find the answer if necessary. Begin with *3* items and ask what they need to do to have *5* items in the set and so on.

2. Turn to page 42. Section 1: Tell the students to read the numbers in the box. Ask them to name the shape of the box (rectangle). Tell them to use their red crayon to circle the number *below* the seven (9), the yellow crayon to circle the number to the *right* of

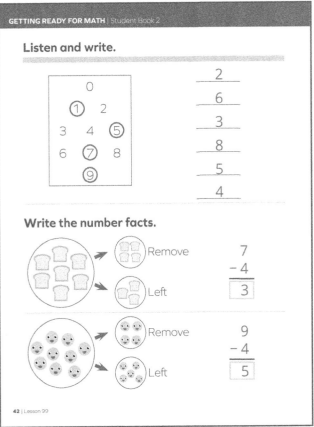

the six (7), the green crayon to circle the number above the eight (5), and the black crayon to circle the number to the *left* of the 2. (1) Section 2: Tell the students that they must write the missing number from the set. Place two sets of *1* and *3* objects in front of the students. Ask them what set is missing in number order. (2) Have them write the *2* on the first line on page 42. Continue with sets of *5* and *7* (6), *2* and *4* (3), *7* and *9* (8), *4* and *6* (5), *3* and *5* (4). Section 3: Ask the students to look at the sets and identify the objects in the sets. Ask them how many are in the first set, how many are removed, and how many are left. Ask them to write a number fact. Do the same for the second set.

3. Turn to page 43. Read the directions with the students. Have them write the number facts.

Student Book 2 | **GETTING READY FOR MATH**

Write the number in the ☐ .

8	9	7	6	5	5
– 6	– 2	– 6	– 1	– 4	– 2
2	7	1	5	1	3

7	8	9	6	9	8
– 1	– 3	– 3	– 2	– 4	– 5
6	5	6	4	5	3

7	6	5	4	7	9
– 2	– 3	– 1	– 2	– 2	– 5
5	3	4	2	5	4

Lesson 99 | **43**

LESSON 100

MATERIALS NEEDED

- pencils
- crayons through orange
- black crayon

Objectives:

1. To write number symbols in number order.

2. To write the signs for add and subtract.

3. To review right, left, above, below.

4. To solve number facts.

Teaching Pages 44, 45, and 46:

1. Turn to page 44. Section 1: Dictate the number symbols *0* through *12* to the students and have them write them on the blank lines. Ask the students if the number symbols are in number order (yes), and have the children read them aloud. Section 2: Tell the children that you are going to dictate two numbers to them and they are to write them in correct number order. Sometimes you may say them in the right order, sometimes you may not. Students may look at the numbers written in order for help. Dictate: *1-0* (0-1), *2-3* (2-3), *9-8* (8-9), *5-4* (4-5), *6-7* (6-7), *4-3* (3-4). Section 3: Ask the students to write the symbol that tells them to add, to subtract. Section 4: Have the students look at the four facts. Tell them the symbol (+, −) is missing. Ask them to write the symbol. Students should use manipulatives to find the answer if necessary. Begin with *3* items and ask what they need to do to have *2* items in the set and so on.

2. Turn to page 45. Section 1: Have the students read the numbers. Tell them they should write the number that comes before and the number that comes after. Section 2: Ask the students to look at the sets and identify the objects in the sets. Ask them how many are in the first set, how many are

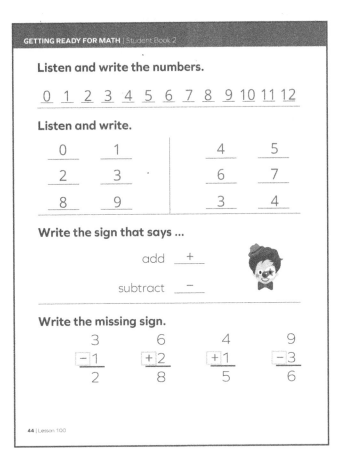

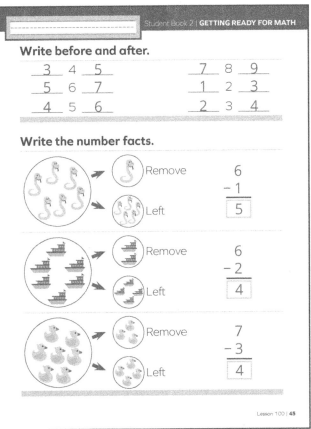

removed, and how many are left. Ask them to write a number fact. Do the same for the next two sets.

3. Turn to page 46. Read the directions with the students. Have them write the number facts.

MATH KINDERGARTEN

Lessons 101–110

LESSON 101

MATERIALS NEEDED

• pencils
• objects for counting

Objectives:

1. To count to 14.

2. To learn about place value for 1's and 10's.

Teaching Pages 47 and 48:

1. Turn to pages 47 and 48. Read the title aloud. Have the children point to the first set of ducks. Have the class count the ducks out loud and then count the marks aloud. Point to the number 10 and state, "This is the number *10*. There are ten ducks and ten marks. Let's count to ten together." Point to the numbers in sequence as the class counts out loud. Repeat this procedure with each set of ducks on pages 47 and 48.

2. Begin a discussion of place value with the students. Have the students make a set of fourteen objects. Ask them to divide the set into two sets, one with ten objects and one with *4* objects. Point to the number *14* on page *48*. Explain to them that in the number *14*, the number symbol *1* stands for a set of *10* objects and the number symbol *4* represents a set of *4* objects. Follow the same procedure working backward with numbers *13-12-11-10*.

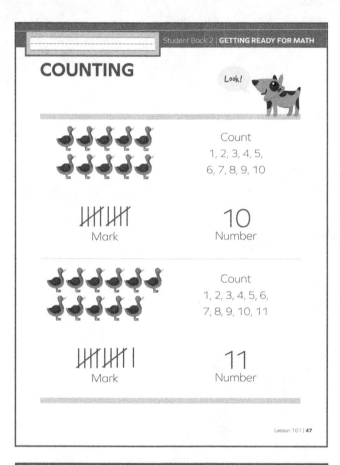

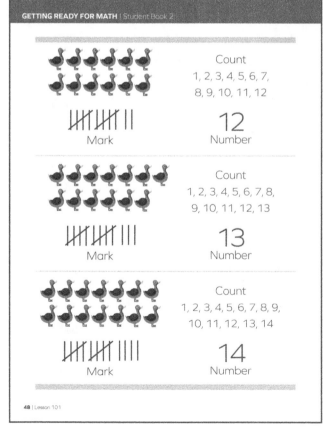

LESSON 102

MATERIALS NEEDED

- pencils
- objects for counting
- addition fact cards to 9

Objectives:

1. To count to 16.

2. To learn about place value for 1's and 10's.

Teaching Pages 49 and 50:

1. Turn to page 49. Have the students read the numbers at the top of the page. Ask if the numbers are in number order. (yes) Read the directions at the top of the page. Tell the class to point to the set of tricycles. Have them make the marks for this set and circle the number at the top of the page. Have them complete the other three sets in the same way. Read the second set of directions with the students. Have the students count the marks out loud and draw a circle around ten marks. Ask the students, "How many sets of tens?" (1) Have the children write the number *1* in the box. Ask them, "How many more?" (3) Have them write the *3* in the box. Ask them to read the number. (13) Follow the same steps to complete the page.

2. Turn to page 50. Tell the children to point to the first set of ducks and then follow the same procedures for *15* and *16* as they did in Lesson 101. Read the next set of directions with the students. Tell the students to count the marks out loud and draw a circle around ten marks. Ask the students, "How many sets of tens?" (1) Have the children write the number 1 in the box. Ask them, "How many more?" (4) Have them write the *4* in the box. Ask them to read the number. (14) Follow the same steps to complete the page.

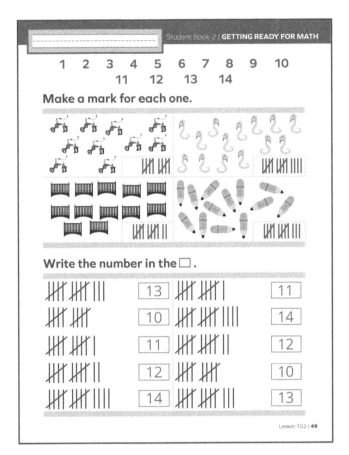

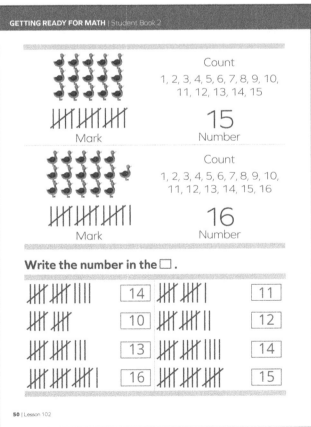

3. At the end of this lesson, review the addition number facts that the students have not mastered. As they commit them to memory, set them aside and concentrate on those with which they are having difficulty. Use objects for counting and visualizing. Allow the students time to give their answers.

LESSON 103

MATERIALS NEEDED

• pencils
• objects for counting
• subtraction fact cards to 9

Objectives:

1. To count to 19.

2. To learn about place value for 1's and 10's.

Teaching Pages 51 and 52:

1. Turn to page 51. Have the children point to the first set of ducks and then follow the same procedures for *17*, *18*, and *19* as they did in Lesson 101.

2. Turn to page 52. Read the directions at the top of the page. Have the class point to the first set on the page. Have them make the marks for this set, and then have them circle the number at the top of the page. Have them complete the other three sets in the same way. Read the second set of directions with the students. Have the students count the marks out loud and circle ten marks. Ask the students, "How many sets of tens?" (1) Have the children write the number *1* in the box. Ask them, "How many more?" (2) Have them write the *2* in the box. Ask them to read the number. (12) Have them complete the page in this manner.

3. At the end of this lesson, review the subtraction number facts that the students have not mastered. As they commit them to memory, set them aside and concentrate on those with which they are having difficulty. Use objects for counting and visualizing. Allow the students time to give their answers.

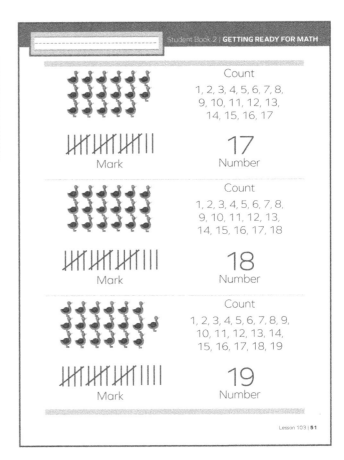

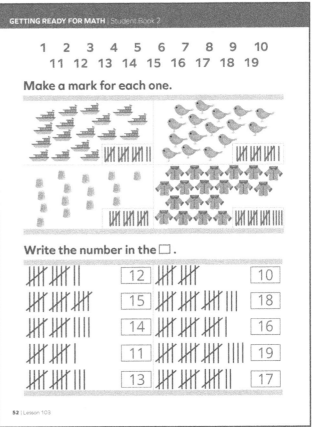

LESSON 104

MATERIALS NEEDED

• pencils

Objectives:

1. To count to 19.

2. To write the number symbols to 19.

Teaching Pages 53 and 54:

1. Turn to page 53. Read the directions at the top of the page. Have the children point to each of the three arrows on the page. Make sure the children understand that they begin counting again at each arrow. Allow the children to complete the page independently.

2. Turn to page 54. Read the first set of directions and have the children write the numbers. Read the second set of directions, and have the children write the numbers. When they have completed this part of the page, go back to the first number in this section and say, "How many tens are there?" (none) "How many more?" (a set of 8) Continue in this manner asking the students to identify each number. For numbers 10 and larger, have them circle ten marks and point to the *1* in the tens' position, and then count how many more and point to that number in the ones' position.

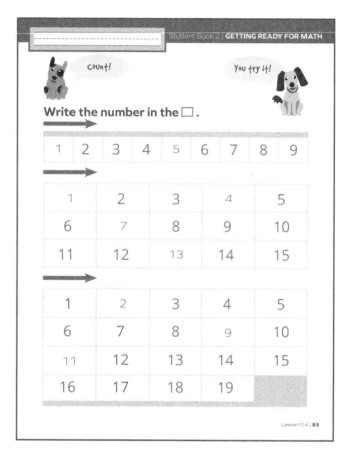

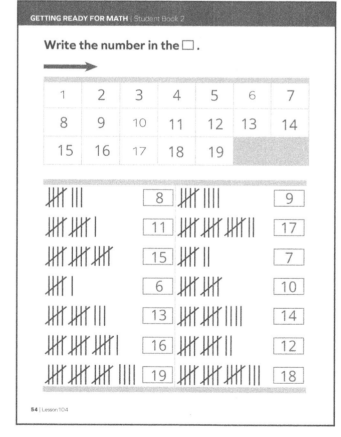

LESSON 105

MATERIALS NEEDED

- pencils
- objects for counting
- set of fact cards for 10's (0 + 10, 1 + 9, 2 + 8, 3 + 7, 4 + 6, 5 + 5, 10 + 0, 9 + 1, 8 + 2, 7 + 3, 6 + 4)
- addition fact cards through 9

Objectives:

1. To add sets and number facts to equal 10.
2. To write numbers before and after to 19.
3. To show number value to 19.

Teaching Pages 55 and 56:

1. Place a set of four objects in front of the students. Ask them to make an addition number fact by dividing the set of four into two sets. (1 + 3, 2 + 2, or 3 + 1) Give them time to discover that there are several combinations they can make. Continue this exercise with six objects, three objects, and seven objects. When the children understand what you have asked them to do, place a set of ten objects in front of them and ask them to make an addition number fact by dividing the set of ten into two sets. Let them make any combination they want (9 + 1, 8 + 2, and so on).

2. Turn to page 55. Read the title of the page. Tell the children to point to the set and count the number of objects. (9) Say out loud, "Add one block." Call attention to the number fact and read it out loud. Tell the children to point to the last set. Have them count the objects in the new set. (10) Say the number fact aloud. "Nine plus one equals ten." Have the students use the *10* objects from the first part of the lesson to illustrate this number fact. Repeat this procedure with each of the sets and number facts on pages 55 and 56. When the set is completed on page 56, have the students

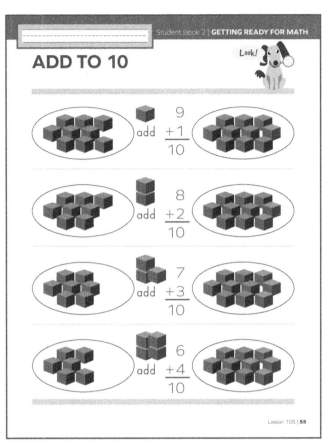

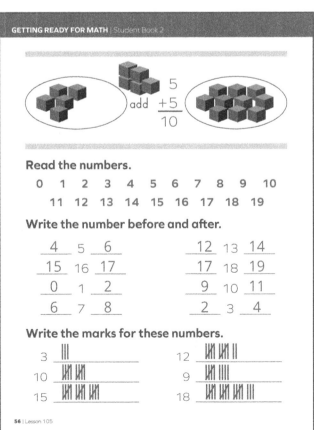

read the numbers *0* through *19* aloud. Ask the students if the numbers are in number order. Ask them questions such as, "What number comes before *15*?" or "What number comes after *18*?" When the students understand what is expected, have them complete the section on the number before and the number after. For the last section, have them make tally marks for each number. Then ask them how many sets of tens are in each one.

3. Introduce the new addition fact cards for ten. Have the students illustrate each one of the fact cards with the *10* objects. Review the addition fact cards for *1* to *9* as necessary.

LESSON 106

MATERIALS NEEDED

- pencils
- crayons colors through black
- new crayon color white

Objectives:

1. To add sets and number facts to equal 10.

2. To learn the new color white.

Teaching Pages 57 and 58:

1. Turn to page 57. Read the directions aloud. Allow the children to complete the page independently.

2. Turn to page 58. Ask the students to identify the picture. Ask whether they think Noah might have taken a lamb with him on the ark. Point to the directions and read them aloud. Have the children make the tally marks and then have them circle the sets of ten.

3. Place the crayons in front of the students. Say each one of the colors red, yellow, green, blue, brown, purple, orange, and black. Ask the students to identify them as you name them. Introduce the new color white. Read the following nursery rhyme, and allow the students to color the picture using the colors they have learned.

> *Mary had a little lamb,*
> *its fleece was white as snow;*
> *And everywhere that Mary went,*
> *the lamb was sure to go.*
> *It followed her to school one day,*
> *that was against the rule;*
> *It made the children laugh and play*
> *to see a lamb at school.*
> *And so the teacher turned it out,*
> *but still it lingered near;*
> *And waited patiently about*
> *till Mary did appear.*
> *"Why does the lamb love Mary so?"*
> *the eager children cry,*
> *"Why Mary loves the lamb, you know,"*
> *the teacher did reply.*

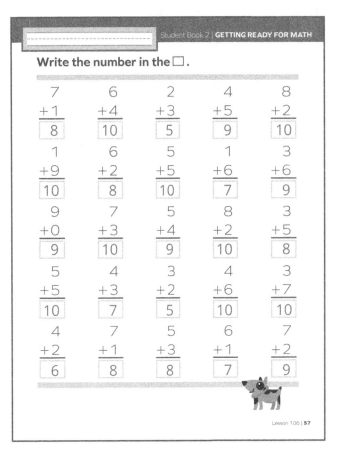

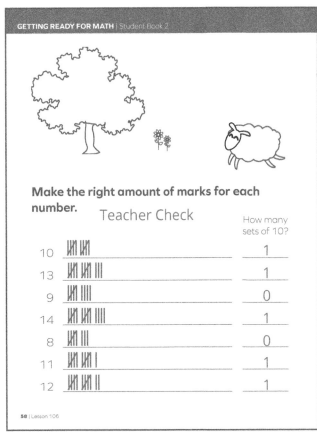

4. The parable of the lost sheep may also be read at this time. (Luke 15:3–7)

LESSON 107

MATERIALS NEEDED

- pencils
- crayons—colors through white
- objects or pictures for 3 pencils, 2 dogs, 2 cats, 9 pieces of candy, 3 drinking glasses

Objectives:

1. To draw sets and number facts to equal 10.

2. To learn to solve story problems.

Teaching Pages 59 and 60:

1. Turn to pages 59 and 60. Call attention to the first row of sets. Have the children point to the first set. Read the directions above it out loud. Tell the children to draw a set of eight tally marks and two tally marks and then write the answer to the number fact. Allow the children to complete the sets independently. Point to the second set of directions on page 60. Tell the children that you are going to give them four problems and ask them to tell you the answers. Explain to the children that these are called *story problems*. Use the objects or pictures to help the children solve the problems.

   1: Jerry gave one pencil to Lisa and two pencils to James. How many pencils altogether did Jerry give to Lisa and James? Point to the first box on page 60. Ask the children to write a number fact about the story. Ask what the first line stands for (Lisa's pencil) and the second line (James's pencils). Ask the students what they need to do to find out how many pencils altogether. (add 1 + 2 = 3) Give them another problem and follow the same procedure.

   2: Jason has two dogs and Laura has two cats. How many animals do they have altogether? Point to the second box on

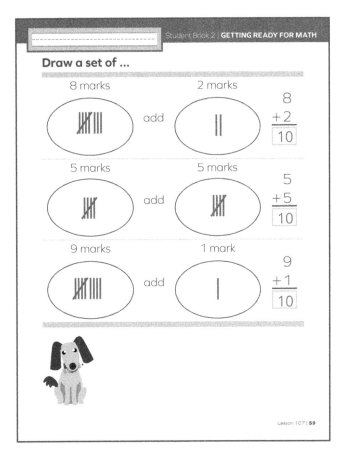

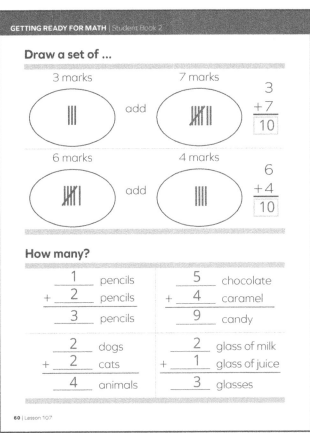

page 60 and have the children follow the steps used in problem 1 to find the answer. (2 + 2 = 4) Continue in the same manner with the next two problems.

3: Mary and Beth bought some candy at the store. Mary bought five pieces of chocolate candy and Beth bought four pieces of caramel. How many pieces of candy did they buy altogether? (5 + 4 = 9)

4: After riding their bicycles, Nathan and Jeremy were very thirsty. Nathan drank two glasses of milk and Jeremy drank one glass of orange juice. How many glasses did they drink altogether? (2 + 1 = 3)

LESSON 108

MATERIALS NEEDED

• pencils
• paper bag
• group of 25 small objects

Objectives:

1. To count sets of 10.

2. To learn to estimate objects to 19.

3. To identify big and little.

Teaching Pages 61 and 62:

1. Turn to page 61. Read the title of the page aloud. Have the children count the blocks at the top of the page. Place a group of objects in front of the children and have them make a set of *10*. Have the children point to the pencils. Read the sentence with the children. Have them count the pencils and write the number on the line. Finish the page in this manner.

2. Turn to page 62. Have the children point to and then read the numbers at the top of the page. Put a group of twenty-five objects in a bag and shake well. Have the students read the first number (7) in the first column on the page and ask them to close their eyes and try to draw that many objects out of the bag. Tell them to put the objects down in front of them. Have the students count the objects and write the number they have drawn in the second column. Then ask them if the number of objects they drew out is the same as, bigger, or smaller than the number *7*. Have them write *S* for the same, *B* for bigger or *L* for smaller (little) in the third column. Continue in the same manner to complete the page. Children should begin to learn by touch the approximate number of objects that they are holding.

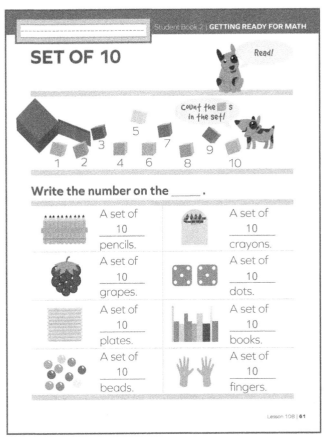

LESSON 109

MATERIALS NEEDED

- pencils
- crayons—colors through white

Objectives:

1. To add number facts to 10.

2. To choose sets of 10.

3. To count to 19.

4. To write number symbols to 19.

Teaching Pages 63 and 64:

1. Turn to page 63. Read each set of directions. Have the students complete the sections as you read the directions.

2. Turn to page 64. State that *10* is a special number because God gave the Ten Commandments to His people. Discuss Moses and the Ten Commandments with the class. Read Exodus 20:1–17 to the children. Have them fill in the numbers for the Ten Commandments in the order they are given in the Bible. They may color the picture using the colors they have learned.

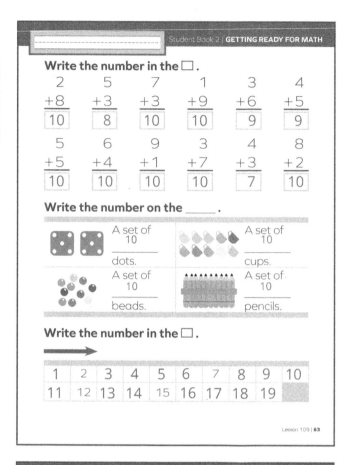

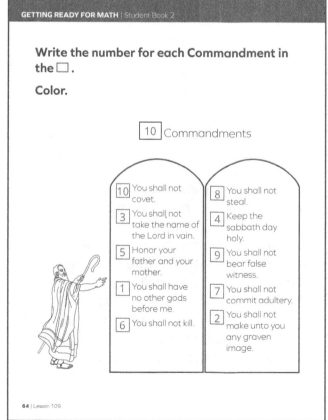

LESSON 110

MATERIALS NEEDED

- pencils
- objects for counting

Objectives:

1. To choose sets of 10.

2. To add numbers to 10 up to 15.

3. To practice addition facts.

Teaching Pages 65, 66, and 67:

1. Write the numbers *0* through *15* on a piece of paper for the students to see. Have the students count ten objects and keep them together in a set. Tell them to read the numbers from the paper aloud. Ask them to point to the number that represents their set of ten. (10) Point to the next number. (11) Ask the children how many objects they would need to add to their set to make eleven. (1) Continue this questioning, beginning each time with a set of ten, and ask how many to add to make twelve (2), thirteen (3), fourteen (4), and fifteen (5).

2. Turn to pages 65 and 66. Tell the children to point to the first set of ice cream cones. Ask the children to count the sets and add them aloud. Point out the corresponding number fact. Show them where the *10* is written and where the *1* is written. Point out where the *11* is written in the answer. Have them read the problem. *Ten plus one equals eleven.* Repeat this procedure for pages 65 and 66. Tell them to complete the exercise at the bottom of page 66.

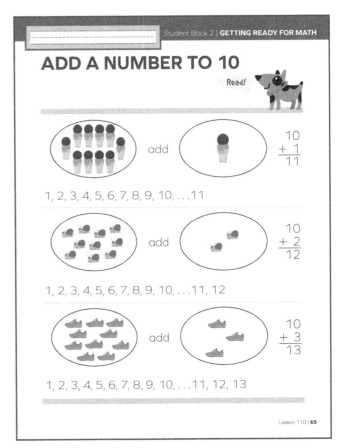

ADD A NUMBER TO 10

Read!

add $\begin{array}{r} 10 \\ + 1 \\ \hline 11 \end{array}$

1, 2, 3, 4, 5, 6, 7, 8, 9, 10, ...11

add $\begin{array}{r} 10 \\ + 2 \\ \hline 12 \end{array}$

1, 2, 3, 4, 5, 6, 7, 8, 9, 10, ...11, 12

add $\begin{array}{r} 10 \\ + 3 \\ \hline 13 \end{array}$

1, 2, 3, 4, 5, 6, 7, 8, 9, 10, ...11, 12, 13

Lesson 110 | **65**

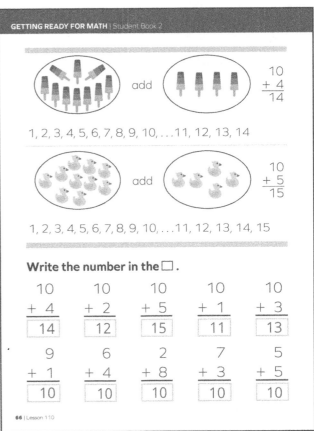

GETTING READY FOR MATH | Student Book 2

add $\begin{array}{r} 10 \\ + 4 \\ \hline 14 \end{array}$

1, 2, 3, 4, 5, 6, 7, 8, 9, 10, ...11, 12, 13, 14

add $\begin{array}{r} 10 \\ + 5 \\ \hline 15 \end{array}$

1, 2, 3, 4, 5, 6, 7, 8, 9, 10, ...11, 12, 13, 14, 15

Write the number in the ☐.

| $\begin{array}{r} 10 \\ + 4 \\ \hline 14 \end{array}$ | $\begin{array}{r} 10 \\ + 2 \\ \hline 12 \end{array}$ | $\begin{array}{r} 10 \\ + 5 \\ \hline 15 \end{array}$ | $\begin{array}{r} 10 \\ + 1 \\ \hline 11 \end{array}$ | $\begin{array}{r} 10 \\ + 3 \\ \hline 13 \end{array}$ |

| $\begin{array}{r} 9 \\ + 1 \\ \hline 10 \end{array}$ | $\begin{array}{r} 6 \\ + 4 \\ \hline 10 \end{array}$ | $\begin{array}{r} 2 \\ + 8 \\ \hline 10 \end{array}$ | $\begin{array}{r} 7 \\ + 3 \\ \hline 10 \end{array}$ | $\begin{array}{r} 5 \\ + 5 \\ \hline 10 \end{array}$ |

66 | Lesson 110

3. Turn to page 67. Dictate the following problems to the students. Be sure that they are lining up the numbers correctly, writing the sign, and drawing the line between the problem and the answer.

Dictate: Ten plus one equals eleven.

```
  10    10    10    10    10
 + 1   + 2   + 3   + 4   + 5
 ----  ----  ----  ----  ----
  11    12    13    14    15
```

4. Read the directions at the bottom of the page, and have the students complete the exercise.

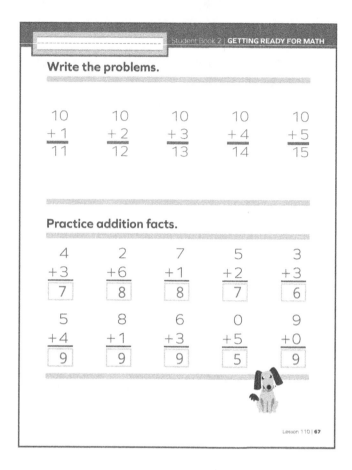

MATH KINDERGARTEN

Lessons 111–120

LESSON 111

MATERIALS NEEDED

- pencils
- objects for counting

Objectives:

1. To choose sets of 10.

2. To add numbers to 10 up to 19.

3. To practice subtraction facts.

Teaching Pages 68 and 69:

1. Write the numbers 0 through 19 on a piece of paper for the students to see. Have the students count ten objects and keep them together in a set. Tell them to read aloud the numbers from the paper. Ask them to point to the number that represents their set of ten. (10) Point to the next number. (11) Ask the children how many objects they would need to add to their set to make eleven. (one) Continue this questioning, beginning each time with a set of ten, and ask how many to add to make twelve (2), thirteen (3), fourteen (4), fifteen (5), sixteen (6), seventeen (7), eighteen (8), and nineteen (9).

2. Turn to page 68 and 69. Have the children point to the first set. Tell them to count the sets and add them aloud. Point out the corresponding number fact. Show them where the 10 is written and where the 6 is written. Point out where the 16 is written in the answer. Have them read the problem. *Ten plus six equals sixteen*. Repeat this procedure for pages 68 and 69.

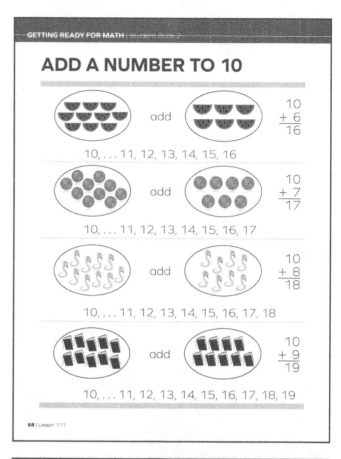

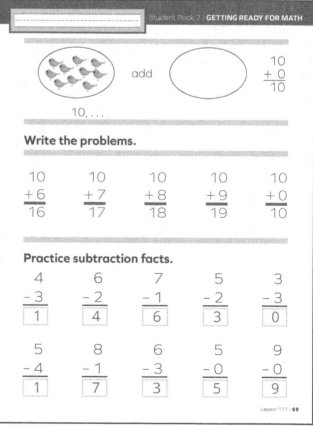

3. Dictate the following problems to the students and have them write them on page 69. Be sure that they are lining up the numbers correctly, writing the sign, and drawing the line between the problem and the answer.

    Dictate: Ten plus six equals sixteen.

    $$
    \begin{array}{ccccc}
    10 & 10 & 10 & 10 & 10 \\
    +\,6 & +\,7 & +\,8 & +\,9 & +\,0 \\
    \hline
    16 & 17 & 18 & 19 & 10
    \end{array}
    $$

4. Read the directions at the bottom of the page and have the students complete the problems.

LESSON 112

MATERIALS NEEDED

- pencils
- paper
- objects for counting

Objectives:

1. To choose sets of 10.

2. To add numbers to 10 up to 19.

3. To learn about place value for 1's and 10's.

Teaching Pages 70 and 71:

1. Ask the students to use the objects to make a set of ten. Tell the students to write the number that represents the objects in the set on a piece of paper. (10) Point to the *1* and say, "This number tells us how many sets of ten that we have. This is called the tens' place." Point to the *0* and say, "This number tells us how many more we have. It is called the ones' place." Use the same method to show place value for the numbers *eleven* through *nineteen*. Always begin by having the students make a set of objects to represent the number. Have them separate the set of ten from the remainder of the objects to help them understand tens' place and more than ten.

2. Turn to page 70. Read the directions aloud. Ask the children to count the objects in the first set and point to the ten. Ask them to count the objects in the second set and point to the 6. Have them count all of the objects to sixteen. Point to the *1* and ask, "What place is this number in?" (tens') Point to the *0* and say, "What place is this number in?" (ones') Point to the *6* and say, "What place is this number in?" (ones') Talk to the students about writing the problem so that the numbers in the ones' place are lined up and the numbers in the tens' place are lined up. Explain that we add the ones' place together first and we add the tens' place

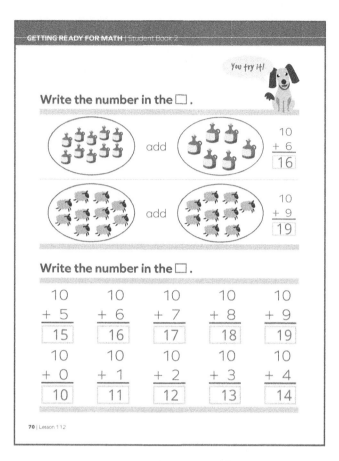

you try it!

Write the number in the ☐ .

		10
	add	+ 6
		16

		10
	add	+ 9
		19

Write the number in the ☐ .

10	10	10	10	10
+ 5	+ 6	+ 7	+ 8	+ 9
15	16	17	18	19
10	10	10	10	10
+ 0	+ 1	+ 2	+ 3	+ 4
10	11	12	13	14

70 | Lesson 112

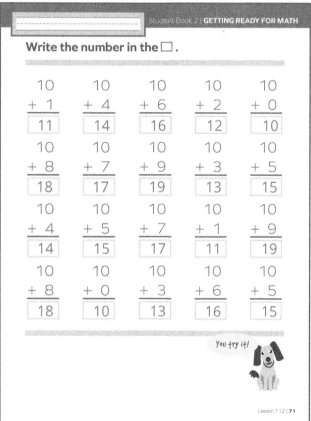

Write the number in the ☐ .

10	10	10	10	10
+ 1	+ 4	+ 6	+ 2	+ 0
11	14	16	12	10
10	10	10	10	10
+ 8	+ 7	+ 9	+ 3	+ 5
18	17	19	13	15
10	10	10	10	10
+ 4	+ 5	+ 7	+ 1	+ 9
14	15	17	11	19
10	10	10	10	10
+ 8	+ 0	+ 3	+ 6	+ 5
18	10	13	16	15

you try it!

Lesson 112 | **71**

together next. Have them say aloud, "Zero plus six is six. One plus zero (nothing) is one. Ten plus six is sixteen." Have the students complete pages 70 and 71 in this manner. Allow the students objects for counting or for making sets if necessary.

LESSON 113

MATERIALS NEEDED

- pencils
- objects for counting
- subtraction fact cards through 9

Objectives:

1. To write the number symbols to 19.

2. To identify place value for ones and tens.

3. To add numbers to 10 up to 19.

4. To subtract number facts to 9.

Teaching Pages 72 and 73:

1. Turn to page 72. Read the first set of directions aloud. Tell the children to write the numbers in number order. Read the second set of directions. Ask the children to point to the first problem and tell what numbers are in the ones' position (zero and zero) and what number is in the tens' position (1). Have the students complete the problems by using objects for counting and/or by adding the numbers in the ones' column and the number in the tens' column.

2. Turn to page 73, and read the instructions aloud. Point out to the students that all the numbers on this page are in the ones' position. Remind them that these problems are like their fact cards. Have them review a few of their subtraction fact cards, and then have them complete page 73.

Write the number in the ☐.

→

1	2	3	4	5
6	7	8	9	10
11	12	13	14	15
16	17	18	19	

$$\begin{array}{r} 10 \\ +\ 0 \\ \hline 10 \end{array} \quad \begin{array}{r} 10 \\ +\ 3 \\ \hline 13 \end{array} \quad \begin{array}{r} 10 \\ +\ 9 \\ \hline 19 \end{array} \quad \begin{array}{r} 10 \\ +\ 6 \\ \hline 16 \end{array} \quad \begin{array}{r} 10 \\ +\ 2 \\ \hline 12 \end{array}$$

$$\begin{array}{r} 10 \\ +\ 4 \\ \hline 14 \end{array} \quad \begin{array}{r} 10 \\ +\ 8 \\ \hline 18 \end{array} \quad \begin{array}{r} 10 \\ +\ 1 \\ \hline 11 \end{array} \quad \begin{array}{r} 10 \\ +\ 7 \\ \hline 17 \end{array} \quad \begin{array}{r} 10 \\ +\ 5 \\ \hline 15 \end{array}$$

72 | Lesson 113

Write the number in the ☐.

$$\begin{array}{r} 9 \\ -\ 1 \\ \hline 8 \end{array} \quad \begin{array}{r} 4 \\ -\ 1 \\ \hline 3 \end{array} \quad \begin{array}{r} 8 \\ -\ 4 \\ \hline 4 \end{array} \quad \begin{array}{r} 6 \\ -\ 4 \\ \hline 2 \end{array} \quad \begin{array}{r} 4 \\ -\ 3 \\ \hline 1 \end{array}$$

$$\begin{array}{r} 6 \\ -\ 5 \\ \hline 1 \end{array} \quad \begin{array}{r} 8 \\ -\ 1 \\ \hline 7 \end{array} \quad \begin{array}{r} 3 \\ -\ 2 \\ \hline 1 \end{array} \quad \begin{array}{r} 7 \\ -\ 4 \\ \hline 3 \end{array} \quad \begin{array}{r} 8 \\ -\ 5 \\ \hline 3 \end{array}$$

$$\begin{array}{r} 7 \\ -\ 3 \\ \hline 4 \end{array} \quad \begin{array}{r} 9 \\ -\ 8 \\ \hline 1 \end{array} \quad \begin{array}{r} 2 \\ -\ 1 \\ \hline 1 \end{array} \quad \begin{array}{r} 8 \\ -\ 2 \\ \hline 6 \end{array} \quad \begin{array}{r} 9 \\ -\ 1 \\ \hline 8 \end{array}$$

$$\begin{array}{r} 9 \\ -\ 5 \\ \hline 4 \end{array} \quad \begin{array}{r} 7 \\ -\ 2 \\ \hline 5 \end{array} \quad \begin{array}{r} 4 \\ -\ 2 \\ \hline 2 \end{array} \quad \begin{array}{r} 5 \\ -\ 1 \\ \hline 4 \end{array} \quad \begin{array}{r} 6 \\ -\ 3 \\ \hline 3 \end{array}$$

$$\begin{array}{r} 8 \\ -\ 5 \\ \hline 3 \end{array} \quad \begin{array}{r} 9 \\ -\ 4 \\ \hline 5 \end{array} \quad \begin{array}{r} 6 \\ -\ 2 \\ \hline 4 \end{array} \quad \begin{array}{r} 9 \\ -\ 3 \\ \hline 6 \end{array} \quad \begin{array}{r} 8 \\ -\ 3 \\ \hline 5 \end{array}$$

Lesson 113 | **73**

LESSON 114

MATERIALS NEEDED

• pencils
• objects for counting
• addition fact cards through 10
• subtraction fact cards through 9
• crayons for coloring through white

Objectives:

1. To add number facts to 10.

2. To subtract number facts to 9.

Teaching Pages 74 and 75:

1. Begin today's lesson with a review of the fact cards for addition and subtraction. Spend as much time as possible, but stop before the children tire of the exercise.

2. Turn to page 74. Read the directions with the students, and have them complete the number facts. Tell them to color the clouds using the colors indicated.

3. Turn to page 75. Read the directions, and have the students complete the facts. Let them color the page using the colors they have learned.

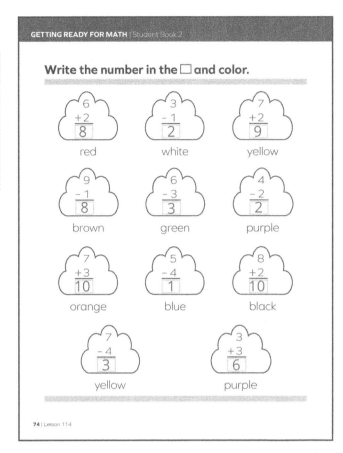

LESSON 115

MATERIALS NEEDED

- pencils
- clock constructed in Lesson 93

Objectives:

1. To tell the hour on the clock.

2. To identify numbers before and after to 19.

3. To add numbers to 10 up to 19.

Teaching Pages 76 and 77:

1. Turn to page 76. Have the students point to the face of the clock from Lesson 93 and read the numbers on the clock. Have them point to the long hand and the short hand. Remind them that the long hand is on the twelve and the short hand is on the number of the hour. Have them turn the hands on their clock to show six o'clock. Point to the first clock on page 76 and ask the children to tell the time on this clock. (six o'clock) Have them complete the exercise by writing the number of the hour on the line. Tell them to say the time aloud as they complete the problems. Read the next set of directions and have the children complete the page.

2. Turn to page 77. Have the students read the numbers at the top of the page. Ask them if these numbers are in number order. (Yes) Pick certain numbers at random and ask what number comes before and what number comes after. Read the directions and have the students complete the first exercise. Read the second set of directions and have them complete that exercise.

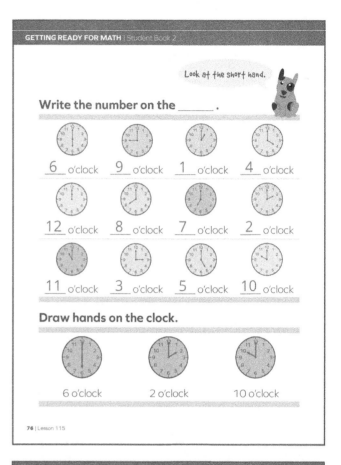

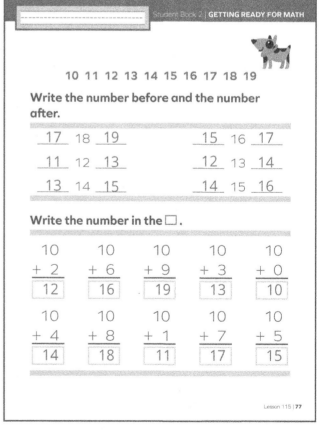

LESSON 116

MATERIALS NEEDED

- pencils
- objects for counting

Objectives:

1. To add number facts to 10.

2. To identify place value.

3. To add numbers to 10 up to 19.

4. To find the big number.

Teaching Pages 78 and 79:

1. Turn to page 78 and 79. Point to the numbers at the top of page 78. Identify 3 + 4 as a number fact. Tell the children to look at the next numbers (10 + 0 = 10, 10 + 6 = 16). Tell them to point to the numbers in the ones' place and the tens' place. Have the children complete the number facts on pages 78 and 79. The middle problems on page 79 may be solved by counting or by adding the ones' column and then the tens' column. Read the directions at the bottom of page 79 to the students and have them complete the exercise. Students who have difficulty in completing the last exercise should make sets of objects to represent the numbers so they can more easily identify which number is larger.

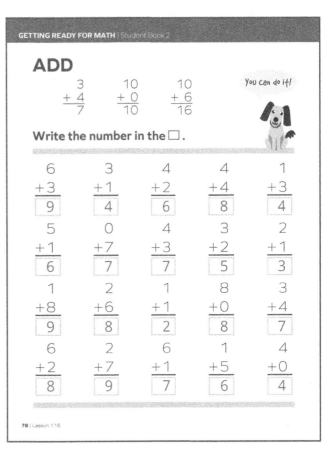

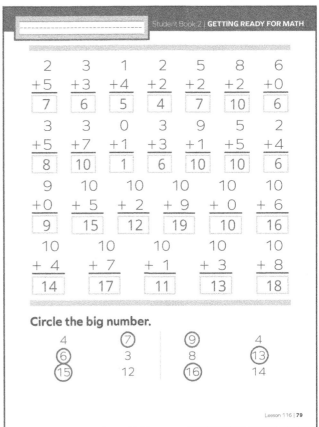

LESSON 117

MATERIALS NEEDED

• pencils
• objects for counting

Objectives:

1. To add number facts to 10 horizontally.

2. To add numbers to 10 up to 19 horizontally.

Teaching Pages 80 and 81:

1. Turn to page 80 and 81. Point to the numbers at the top of page 80. Explain to the children that these numbers are the same as the numbers on the top of page 78, but they are written differently. Allow the children time to make the comparison. Ask them if they can find the same number fact on both pages even though they are written differently. Tell them the answer to the number facts is the same. Have the students complete the number facts on pages 80 and 81. Allow them to refer back to pages 78 and 79. Those students who have difficulty in completing the horizontal problems for 10's may write the problems vertically or use objects for counting.

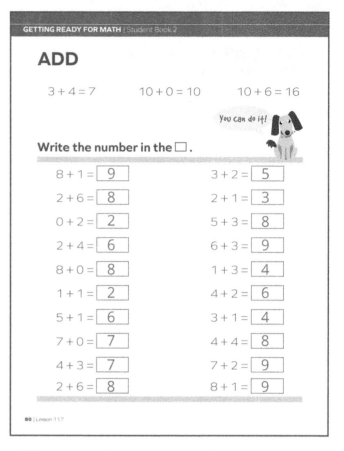

LESSON 118

MATERIALS NEEDED

- pencils
- objects for counting

Objectives:

1. To count to 19.

2. To add number facts to 10.

3. To write the hour on the clock.

4. To add a number to 10 up to 19.

Teaching Pages 82 and 83:

1. Turn to pages 82 and 83. Read the first set of directions, allow the students to complete the exercise, and then read the next set of directions. Proceed in this manner until both pages are completed.

2. Try to give the students as little help as possible.

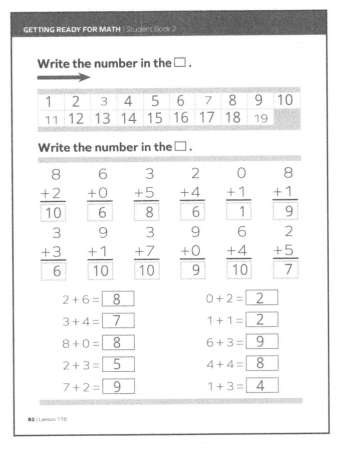

GETTING READY FOR MATH | Student Book 2

Write the number in the ☐.

→

| 1 | 2 | 3 | 4 | 5 | 6 | 7 | 8 | 9 | 10 |
| 11 | 12 | 13 | 14 | 15 | 16 | 17 | 18 | 19 | |

Write the number in the ☐.

8	6	3	2	0	8
+2	+0	+5	+4	+1	+1
10	6	8	6	1	9

3	9	3	9	6	2
+3	+1	+7	+0	+4	+5
6	10	10	9	10	7

$2+6=8$ $0+2=2$

$3+4=7$ $1+1=2$

$8+0=8$ $6+3=9$

$2+3=5$ $4+4=8$

$7+2=9$ $1+3=4$

82 | Lesson 118

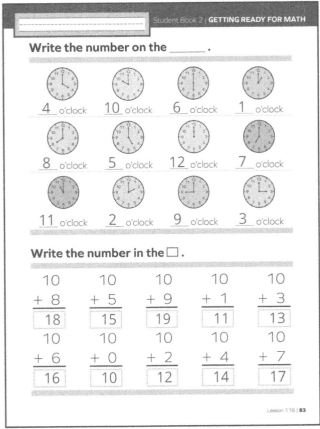

Student Book 2 | **GETTING READY FOR MATH**

Write the number on the _____ .

4 o'clock   10 o'clock   6 o'clock   1 o'clock

8 o'clock   5 o'clock   12 o'clock   7 o'clock

11 o'clock   2 o'clock   9 o'clock   3 o'clock

Write the number in the ☐.

10	10	10	10	10
+ 8	+ 5	+ 9	+ 1	+ 3
18	15	19	11	13

10	10	10	10	10
+ 6	+ 0	+ 2	+ 4	+ 7
16	10	12	14	17

Lesson 118 | 83

LESSON 119

MATERIALS NEEDED

- pencils
- objects for counting

Objectives:

1. To count to 19.

2. To add number facts to 10.

3. To write the hour on the clock.

4. To add a number to 10 up to 19.

Teaching Pages 84, 85, and 86:

1. Turn to pages 84, 85, and 86. Read the first set of directions, allow the students to complete the exercise, and then read the next set of directions. Proceed in this manner until the pages are completed. Try to give the students as little help as possible.

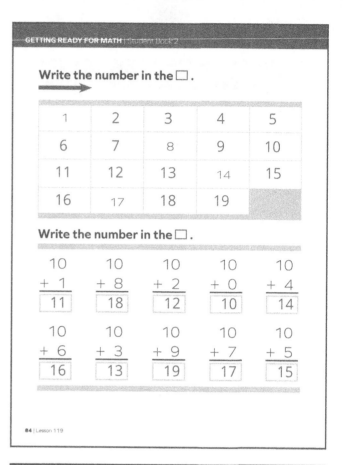

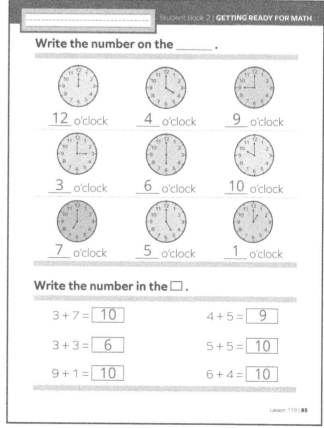

GETTING READY FOR MATH | Student Book 2

Write the number in the ☐ .

6	7	3	4	1	4
+3	+2	+1	+4	+3	+2
9	9	4	8	4	6

4	5	0	5	3	2
+3	+1	+7	+3	+2	+1
7	6	7	8	5	3

1	8	3	0	2	8
+1	+0	+4	+2	+6	+0
2	8	7	2	8	8

6	1	4	2	6	2
+2	+5	+0	+3	+1	+7
8	6	4	5	7	9

86 | Lesson 119

231

LESSON 120

MATERIALS NEEDED

- pencils
- crayons—colors through white

Objectives:

1. To count to 9.
2. To follow directions.
3. To match number words and symbols.
4. To write numbers in number order.

Teaching Pages 87, 88, and 89:

1. Turn to page 87. Talk about the pictures on the page and what the rabbit is doing. Ask the children what they think would be the most fun thing to do. Read the directions to the students and have them write the numbers in the boxes. Ask them to identify the shapes at the top of the page (circle, square, triangle, rectangle). Tell them to use their pencils for this exercise. Find the rabbit jumping *over* the *yellow* seven. Draw a *triangle* around the seven. Find the *big red* four riding on wheels. Draw a *circle* around one wheel. Find the rabbit using binoculars to the *left* of the rabbit and the snake. Draw a *rectangle* around the binoculars. Find the rabbit rowing a boat at the *bottom* of the page. Draw a *square* around the rabbit.

2. Turn to page 88. Section 1: Read the directions with the students. Have them read the number symbols and the number words aloud. Let them complete the exercise independently.

3. Section 2: Read the directions. Explain to the students that they should write the numbers in number order.

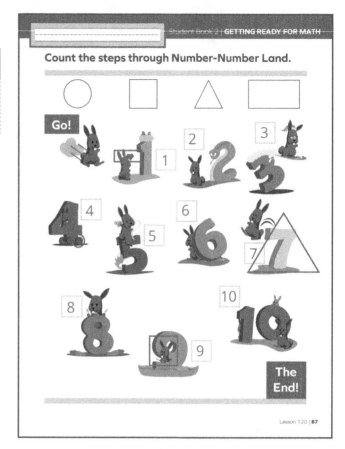

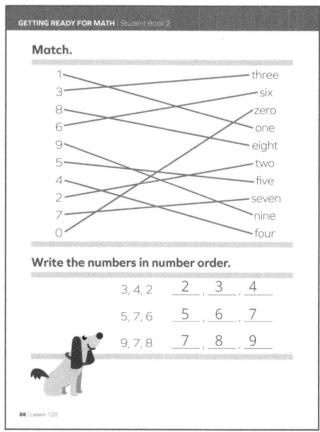

MATH KINDERGARTEN

Lessons 121–130

LESSON 121

MATERIALS NEEDED

- pencils
- addition number facts
- number word cards

Objectives:

1. To subtract with words to nine.

2. To review addition facts.

Teaching Pages 90 and 91:

1. Have the class point to the first box on page 90. Read the caption at the bottom of the box. Tell the children to point to the blocks. Say, "One block subtracted from one block." Emphasize the two ways to write this number fact shown at the right side of the box: *1 – 1* and *one – one*. Have the class read these number facts out loud as they point to them. Repeat this procedure with the remaining sets on page 90, and review 6 – 1, 7 – 1, 8 – 1, and 9 – 1 with the children.

2. Turn to page 91. Have the students read the number words at the top of the page. Read the directions. Ask the students to read the first number fact aloud and say the answer. Then have them write the answer on the lines. Allow them to complete the page independently.

3. Play a game of concentration with selected addition number facts and the number word cards.

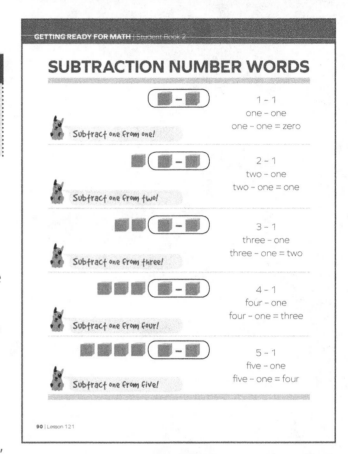

LESSON 122

MATERIALS NEEDED

• pencils
• subtraction number facts
• number word cards

Objectives:

1. To subtract with words to nine.

2. To review subtraction facts.

Teaching Pages 92 and 93:

1. Have the class point to the first box on page 92. Read the caption at the bottom of the box. Tell the children to point to the blocks. Say, "Two blocks subtracted from two blocks." Emphasize the two ways to write this number fact shown at the right side of the box: *2 – 2* and *two – two*. Have the class read these number facts out loud as they point to them. Repeat this procedure with the remaining sets on page 92, and review 7 – 2, 8 – 2, and 9 – 2 with the children.

2. Turn to page 93. Read the directions. Tell the students to read the first number fact aloud and say the answer. Then tell them to write the answer on the lines. Allow them to complete the page independently. They may refer to page 91 if necessary to spell the number words.

3. Play a game of concentration with selected subtraction number facts and number word cards.

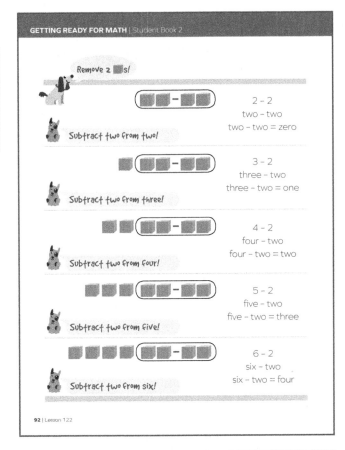

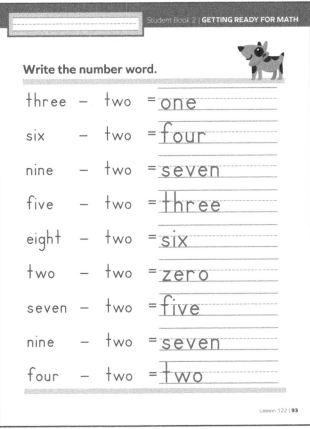

LESSON 123

MATERIALS NEEDED

- pencils
- objects for counting

Objectives:

1. To subtract with number words to nine.

2. To write the number words between.

Teaching Pages 94 and 95:

1. Have the class point to the first box on page 94. Read the caption at the bottom of the box. Tell the children to point to the blocks. Say, "Three blocks subtracted from three blocks." Emphasize the two ways to write this number fact shown at the right side of the box: *3 – 3* and *three – three*. Have the class read these number facts out loud as they point to them. Repeat this procedure with the remaining sets on page 94, and review 8 – 3 and 9 – 3 with the children.

2. Turn to page 95. Read the first set of directions. Tell the students to read the first number fact aloud and say the answer. Then tell them to write the answer on the lines and complete this exercise. Read the second set of directions. Talk to the students about number order. Have them use sets of objects for counting as they complete this exercise.

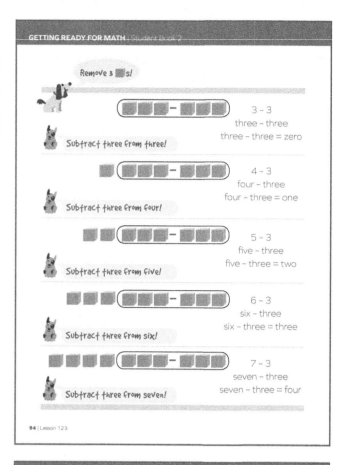

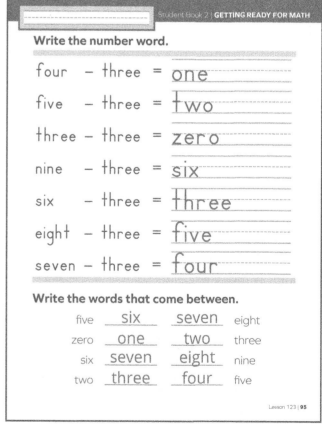

LESSON 124

MATERIALS NEEDED

- pencils
- paper
- objects for counting

Objectives:

1. To subtract with number words to nine.

2. To write numbers in number order.

Teaching Pages 96 and 97:

1. Have the class point to the first box on page 96. Read the caption at the bottom of the box. Tell the children to point to the blocks. Say, "Four blocks subtracted from four blocks." Emphasize the two ways to write this number fact shown at the right side of the box: *4 – 4* and *four – four*. Have the class read these number facts out loud as they point to them. Repeat this procedure with the remaining sets on page 96.

2. Dictate the numbers (zero to nine) to the children in any order. Tell them to write the number symbols on paper. After you have dictated all numbers, have the children write the number symbols as number words in correct number order. Do not allow them to look at page 91 for this exercise.

3. Turn to page 97. Read the instructions with the students. Allow the children to complete the page independently.

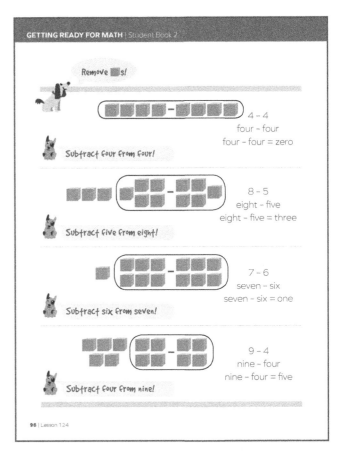

Remove ■s!

4 – 4
four – four
four – four = zero

Subtract four from four!

8 – 5
eight – five
eight – five = three

Subtract five from eight!

7 – 6
seven – six
seven – six = one

Subtract six from seven!

9 – 4
nine – four
nine – four = five

Subtract four from nine!

96 | Lesson 124

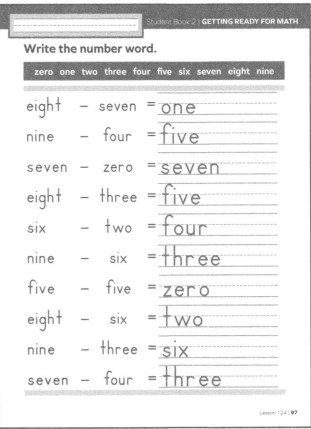

Student Book 2 | **GETTING READY FOR MATH**

Write the number word.

zero one two three four five six seven eight nine

eight	– seven	= one
nine	– four	= five
seven	– zero	= seven
eight	– three	= five
six	– two	= four
nine	– six	= three
five	– five	= zero
eight	– six	= two
nine	– three	= six
seven	– four	= three

Lesson 124 | **97**

243

LESSON 125

MATERIALS NEEDED

- pencils
- objects for counting
- subtraction fact cards to 9
- a set of subtraction fact cards for 10 (10 − 0, 10 − 1, 10 − 2, 10 − 3, 10 − 4, 10 − 5, 10 − 6, 10 − 7, 10 − 8, 10 − 9, 10 − 10
- new number word card for 10

Objectives:

1. To subtract with words to nine.

2. To subtract numbers to 10.

Teaching Pages 98 and 99:

1. Turn to page 98. Have the students select a group of ten objects. Tell them to count the number of objects in the first set on page 98. (10) Ask how many are being taken away. (1) Have the children take one away from their set of ten objects and ask how many are left. (9) Count the objects in the second set on page 98. (9) Point to the number fact and have the children read it aloud. *Ten minus one equals nine.* Point to the first number fact in the box. Ask the students how many are being taken away. Tell the children to remove two from their set of ten objects and ask how many are left. Tell them to write the number in the box and then have them say the number fact. *Ten minus two equals eight.* Have the students continue in this manner until they complete the page. Introduce the set of subtraction fact cards to the children and go through them once.

2. Turn to page 99. Read the directions. Tell the students to read the first number word fact aloud and say the answer. Have them read the number symbol fact aloud and say the answer. Tell them to complete the page following the examples, writing the answer to the number fact in words and then writing the fact in number symbols.

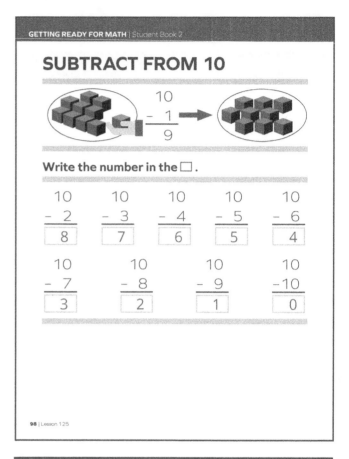

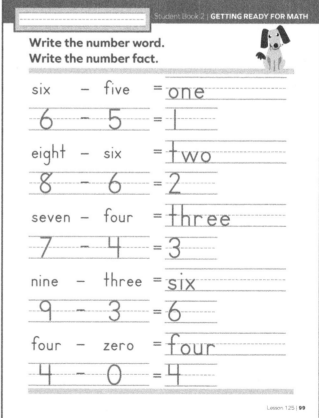

LESSON 126

MATERIALS NEEDED

- pencils
- objects for counting

Objectives:

1. To count the numbers 1 to 20.
2. To write the number symbols 1 to 20.

Teaching Pages 100 and 101:

1. Turn to page 100. Read each set of instructions out loud. Ask the children to count as they point to the numbers. Introduce the number *20* to them. Read the final statement. One more than *19* is *20*. Say, "What number comes after nine?" Ask the children to write this number on the line. Say, "What number comes after nineteen?" Ask the children to write this number on the line. Give the students the objects for counting. Have them select one object at a time and count to twenty.

2. Turn to page 101. Read the first set of instructions. Tell the class to write *1* in the first box. Allow the children to complete the activity independently. Read the next set of instructions with the children. Draw a diagram on the board to illustrate how to connect dots in order. When the children understand what is expected of them, allow them to complete the illustration by drawing dot-to-dot. Read the following nursery rhymes to them as they draw and ask them to identify the characters in the illustration when their drawing is complete.

> *Hey, diddle, diddle,*
> *The cat and the fiddle,*
> *The cow jumped over the moon.*

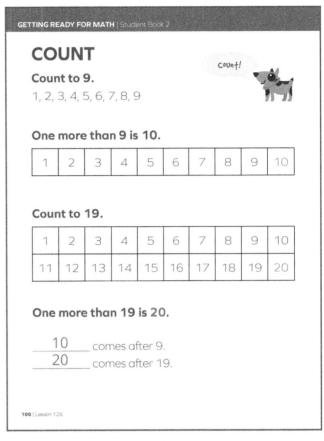

COUNT

Count to 9.

1, 2, 3, 4, 5, 6, 7, 8, 9

count!

One more than 9 is 10.

1	2	3	4	5	6	7	8	9	10

Count to 19.

1	2	3	4	5	6	7	8	9	10
11	12	13	14	15	16	17	18	19	20

One more than 19 is 20.

____10____ comes after 9.

____20____ comes after 19.

100 | Lesson 126

Student Book 2 | **GETTING READY FOR MATH**

Write the number in the ☐ .

➡ **Count to 20.**

1	2	3	4	5	6	7	8	9	10
11	12	13	14	15	16	17	18	19	20

Draw dot-to-dot.

Lesson 126 | **101**

The little dog laughed
To see such sport,
And the dish ran away with the spoon.

Humpty Dumpty sat on a wall,
Humpty Dumpty had a great fall.
All the king's horses,
And all the king's men,
Couldn't put Humpty together again.

LESSON 127

MATERIALS NEEDED

- pencils
- objects for counting
- current calendar

Objectives:

1. To count the numbers 1 to 30.

2. To learn about place value for 10's and 1's.

3. To write the number symbols 1 to 30.

4. To learn about the calendar.

Teaching Pages 102 and 103:

1. Let the children use objects for counting to show that twenty is equal to two sets of ten. Ask them how many more objects they would need to make twenty-one, twenty-two, and so on to twenty-nine. Have them illustrate their answers by using the objects.

2. Turn to page 102. Tell the children to point to the first problem (20 + 1). Point to the *2* and ask, "What is the place value of this number?" (tens') Explain to the children that the *2* means there are two sets of ten. Let them look at their sets of objects again. Point to the *1* and ask, "What is the place value of this number?" (ones') State, "Twenty plus one equals twenty-one." Have the class repeat it. Continue this procedure for each problem. Tell the students to point to each number at the bottom of the page and count out loud to *30*. Emphasize, "One more than twenty-nine is thirty."

3. Have the children use their objects for counting to show that three groups of ten equals thirty.

4. Turn to page 103. Read the directions, and have the students complete the first exercise on the page.

5. Introduce the *current* calendar to the students. Ask them how many months they

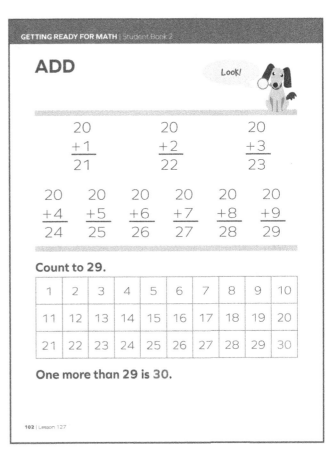

can name and which months are special to them. (You will receive a better response to this question if you associate months with special occasions; for example, birthdays and holidays.) Talk about the number of days in a week and ask the children if they can name the days in order. Point to the *current* calendar and show the number of days in a month. Ask the children to find today's date. Continue on page 103. Point to the second exercise on the page and have the students describe the chart (calendar). Read the month and the days of the week with them. Tell them to write the numbers. When they have finished, ask them to say the dates (numbers) for Sunday (6, 13, 20, 27), Monday, Tuesday, and so on.

LESSON 128

MATERIALS NEEDED

- pencils
- objects for counting
- crayons—colors through white

Objectives:

1. To count the numbers 1 to 40.

2. To learn about place value for 10's and 1's.

3. To write the number symbols 1 to 40.

Teaching Pages 104 and 105:

1. Begin today's lesson by having the children use objects to count to ten. Tell them to place the set of ten aside. Have them continue counting with objects to eleven, twelve, until they reach twenty. Place that group of ten objects aside. Continue counting with twenty-one until they reach thirty and put that group of ten objects aside. Continue counting with thirty-one until they reach forty and put that group of ten objects aside.

2. Turn to page 104. Tell the children to point to each number fact and read it aloud with the teacher. Have the children count out loud to *40*. As they reach *10*, show them the set of objects they have made for ten, then point to the *1* in the tens' position and the *0* in the ones' position. Tell them to say, "I have one set of ten and no ones." Repeat this procedure as they count to *20, 30, 40*.

3. Turn to page 105. Read the first set of instructions. Call attention to the 1 and 40 already written in the boxes. Have the children write the numbers and fill in the blank lines in the middle of the page.

4. Read the final set of instructions aloud. Allow the children to color the illustration when they have completed connecting the dots.

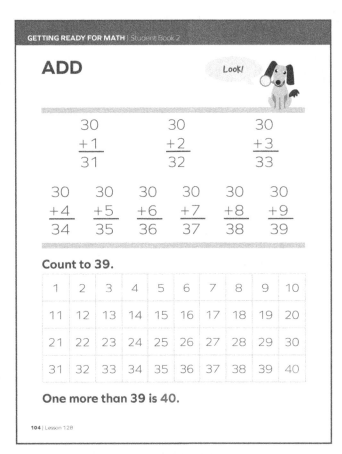

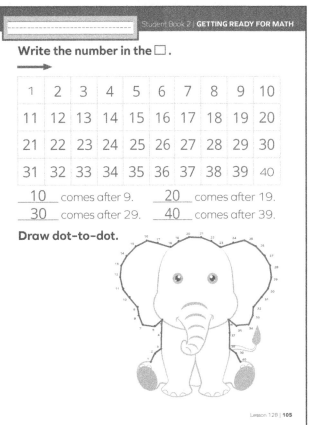

LESSON 129

MATERIALS NEEDED

• pencils
• objects for counting

Objectives:

1. To count the numbers 1 to 50.

2. To learn about place value for 10's and 1's.

3. To write the number symbols 1 to 50.

4. To write missing numbers to 50.

Teaching Pages 106 and 107:

1. Follow the same procedure in this lesson as in Lesson 128 counting objects, grouping them in tens through fifty.

2. Turn to page 106. Have the children point to each number fact and count to *50*. Have them associate the counting with their groups of ten objects. Point out the tens' position and how it sequences from *1-2-3-4-5*.

3. Turn to page 107. Read the first set of instructions. Call attention to the *1* already written in the box. Have the children write the numbers and fill in the blank lines in the middle of the page. Read the directions at the bottom of the page. Tell the children to use their charts to find the missing numbers.

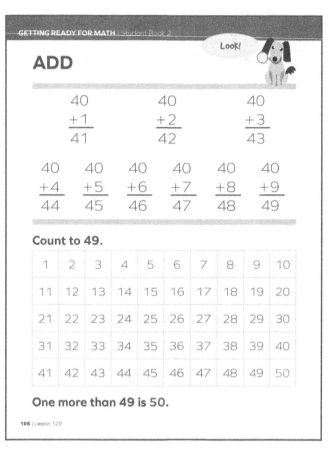

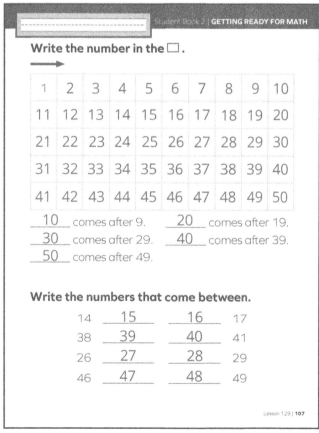

LESSON 130

MATERIALS NEEDED

- pencils
- objects for counting
- number symbol cards
- addition and subtraction fact cards

Objectives:

1. To write the number symbols 1 to 50.

2. To subtract with number words and number symbols to nine horizontally.

3. To write missing numbers to 50.

Teaching Pages 108 and 109:

1. Turn to pages 108 and 109. Read each set of instructions aloud. The children may use objects for counting to complete the subtraction exercises. They may refer to the chart they have completed on page 108 for the missing numbers exercise. Play several games of concentration when these pages are completed. Use addition and subtraction fact cards and number symbol cards.

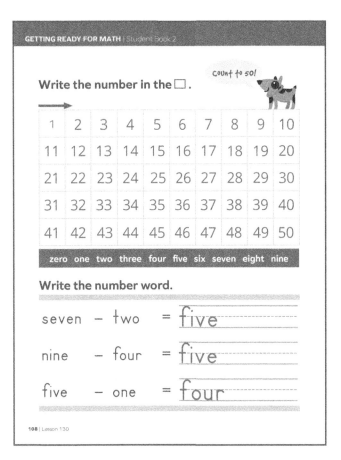

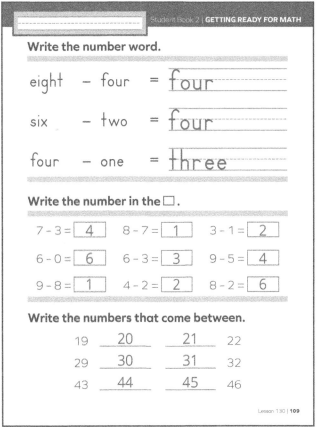

MATH KINDERGARTEN

Lessons 131–140

LESSON 131

MATERIALS NEEDED

- pencils
- objects for counting
- chart of numbers 1 to 50

Objective:

To identify the number that comes before and after to 50.

Teaching Pages 110 and 111:

1. A chart of numbers is helpful for the next group of lessons. The chart from page 106 may be cut out, pasted on cardboard, and displayed for the children.

2. Turn to page 110. Have the children point to the first row of numbers and read the numbers aloud.

3. Say, "Seven is before eight. Nine is after eight." Repeat this procedure for the other examples using the chart for reference. Then have the students complete the page by circling the correct number as you read.

Circle the number ...

1.	41	42	43	1. after 42.
2.	16	17	18	2. before 17.
3.	5	6	7	3. before 6.
4.	30	31	32	4. after 31.
5.	24	25	26	5. after 25.

4. Turn to page 111. Read the first set of instructions out loud. Have the children read the numbers and circle the correct answer. Read the second set of instructions and follow the same procedure. Read the final set of instructions and have the students complete the page. Allow them to use the chart of numbers 1 to 50.

NUMBER ORDER (BEFORE, AFTER)

Before		After
(7)	8	9
	7 is before 8.	
14	15	(16)
	16 is after 15.	
(21)	22	23
	21 is before 22.	
36	37	(38)
	38 is after 37.	
41	42	(43)
(16)	17	18
(5)	6	7
30	31	(32)
24	25	(26)

110 | Lesson 131

Student Book 2 | **GETTING READY FOR MATH**

Circle the number before.

(7)	<u>8</u>	9	(14)	<u>15</u>	16
(22)	<u>23</u>	24	(27)	<u>28</u>	29
(45)	<u>46</u>	47	(40)	<u>41</u>	42
(33)	<u>34</u>	36	(39)	<u>40</u>	41

Circle the number after.

4	<u>5</u>	(6)	17	<u>18</u>	(19)
12	<u>13</u>	(14)	28	<u>29</u>	(30)
46	<u>47</u>	(48)	35	<u>36</u>	(37)
31	<u>32</u>	(33)	42	<u>43</u>	(44)

Write the number.

after 6	7	before 50	49
before 20	19	after 41	42
after 29	30	after 26	27
after 39	40	before 17	16

Lesson 131 | **111**

LESSON 132

MATERIALS NEEDED

- pencils
- objects for counting
- chart of numbers 1 to 50

Objectives:

1. To write the number symbols 1 to 50.

2. To add and subtract with number words and number symbols to nine horizontally.

3. To write the numbers before and after to 50.

Teaching Pages 112, 113, and 114:

1. Turn to page 112. Read the directions and have the students complete the page. Be sure they read the addition and subtraction symbols correctly.

2. Turn to page 113. Read the directions and have the students complete the page. Be sure they read the addition and subtraction symbols correctly.

3. Turn to page 114. Read each set of directions as the students complete the work.

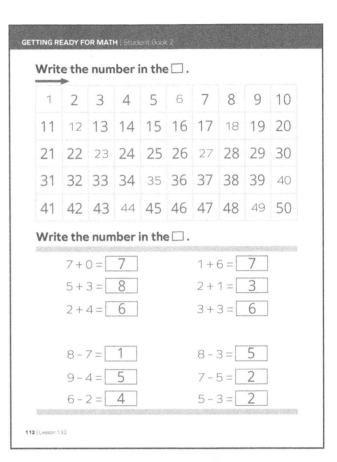

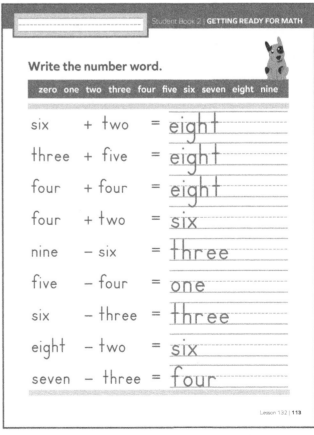

Circle the number before.

(5)	6	7	(36)	37	38
(14)	15	16	(40)	41	42
(22)	23	24	(48)	49	50

Circle the number after.

1	2	(3)	33	34	(35)
9	10	(11)	25	26	(27)
20	21	(22)	42	43	(44)

Write the number.

after 5	6	after 28	29
before 10	9	before 36	35
before 16	15	after 41	42
after 13	14	after 49	50

LESSON 133

MATERIALS NEEDED

- pencils
- clock made in Lesson 93

Objective:

To tell the time of the hour and half-hour.

Teaching Pages 115 and 116:

1. Turn to page 115. Read the title of the page, and then read out loud, "Count to twelve." Have the class count to twelve, pointing to each number as they count. Read out loud, "A clock counts to twelve." Have the class count to twelve, pointing to each number on the clock as they count. State, "We can tell the time of the hour. The long hand is on the twelve." (Have the class point to the long hand on the second clock.) "The short hand points to the hour. On this clock, the short hand is pointing to which number?" (Allow the class to answer.) "The time is three o'clock." Ask the children to move the hands on their clocks to 3 o'clock.

2. Turn to page 116. Read the first set of directions. Have the children point to the first clock. State, "The long hand is on the twelve." "What number is the short hand on?" "What time is it?" Have the class write the correct number on the line. Ask them to illustrate the time on their own clocks. Tell the children to write the time for the rest of the clocks in this exercise. State, "We can tell the time to the half-hour. The long hand is on the six." (Have the class point to the long hand.) "The long hand points to the half-hour. The short hand points to the number of the hour. On this clock, the short hand is pointing to which number?" (Allow the class to answer.) "The time is three thirty." Have the class repeat this time and illustrate the time on their own clocks. Tell them to complete the page writing the correct time to the half-hour. Ask the students to show several examples of how they can use their clocks to illustrate the time to the hour and half-hour.

Student Book 2 | **GETTING READY FOR MATH**

TELL TIME

Count to 12.

| 1 | 2 | 3 | 4 | 5 | 6 | 7 | 8 | 9 | 10 | 11 | 12 |

A clock counts to 12.

**Tell time at the hour. The long hand is on 12.
The short hand is on 3.**

3 o'clock

Lesson 133 | **115**

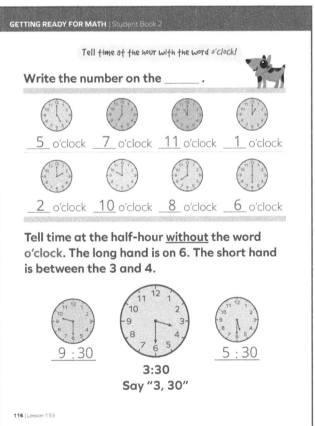

GETTING READY FOR MATH | Student Book 2

Tell time at the hour with the word o'clock!

Write the number on the _____ .

5 o'clock 7 o'clock 11 o'clock 1 o'clock

2 o'clock 10 o'clock 8 o'clock 6 o'clock

Tell time at the half-hour _underline{without}_ the word o'clock. The long hand is on 6. The short hand is between the 3 and 4.

9 : 30   5 : 30

3:30
Say "3, 30"

116 | Lesson 133

LESSON 134

MATERIALS NEEDED

- pencils
- clock made in Lesson 93
- current calendar
- paper
- scissors
- paste or glue
- crayons through white
- pink crayon

Objectives:

1. To tell the time of the half-hour.

2. To make a calendar.

Teaching Pages 117 and 118:

1. Turn to page 117. Read the caption and instructions out loud. Have the children point to the first clock. State, "The long hand is on the six. What number is the short hand on? What time is it?" Point out to the class that the small hand moves with the long hand. Show the clockwise movement. Explain to the children that the hour is always the number that the short hand is moving *away from*. Have the class write the correct number on the line and say the answer aloud. Allow the children to complete this page independently.

2. Introduce the *current* calendar to the children, and review the current year, months, and days of week. Ask the students to select their favorite month (perhaps the months of their birthdays).

3. Turn to page 118. Compare the graph on page 118 to the month of each student's birthday on the *current* calendar. Tell them they are going to make a calendar page just like the months of their birthdays. Read the directions and have the children write the name of the month and the year on the blank lines. Ask the children to point to the days of the week while you say the names

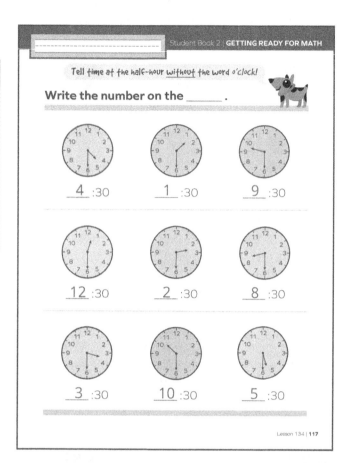

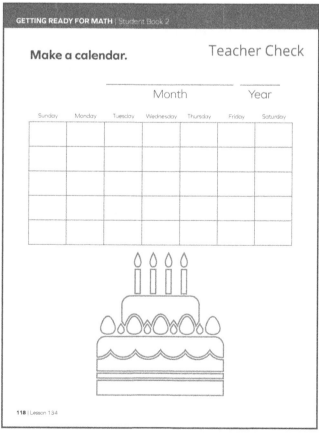

aloud. On a piece of paper, make a chart identical to the one on page 103 (add one space for 31) and have the children write the numbers 1 to 31 in each block. Talk to them about months that have different numbers of days (from 28 to 31). Cut the piece of paper into blocks, and have the children paste the numbers on the chart on page 118 so the number arrangement is the same as the month that they have chosen. Put the crayons through white in front of the students, and have them identify each one as you say the color. Identify the pink crayon for them, and tell them that is their new color. Have them use the pink crayon to draw a circle around the day of their birthday or any other special day. Let the children color the cake at the bottom of the page.

LESSON 135

MATERIALS NEEDED

• pencils
• nine pennies

Objective:

To count pennies.

Teaching Pages 119 and 120:

1. Turn to page 119 and read the title aloud. Start a discussion with the children about the need for and use of money. Place the pennies in front of the students so they may use them as they follow the directions. Tell them that each penny has a value of *one*. Count the first set of pennies out loud. Have the class point to each penny as they count. Emphasize the number words and the number symbols. Repeat this procedure with the second set of pennies. Give the students time to group the pennies in piles and to count them.

2. Turn to page 120. Read the instructions out loud. Have the children count the number of pennies in the first set. Have them make the same set with their pennies. Write the number in the box.

3. Allow the children to complete the page using pennies to illustrate their answers.

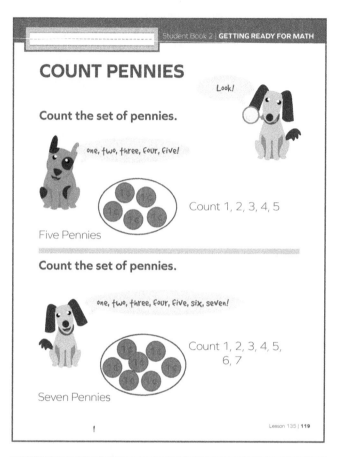

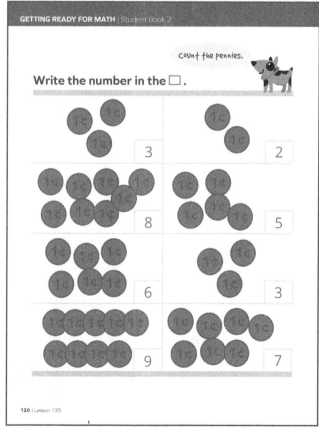

LESSON 136

MATERIALS NEEDED

- pencils
- ten pennies
- nine dimes

Objective:

To count pennies and dimes.

Teaching Pages 121 and 122:

1. Place ten pennies and a dime in front of the students. Explain to them that each dime represents ten pennies. Turn to page 121. Count the first set of dimes out loud as the children point to them. Have the students use their dimes to count the sets. Emphasize the number words and number symbols. Repeat this procedure with the second set of dimes. Give the students time to group the dimes in piles and count them.

2. Turn to page 122. Read the instructions out loud. Have the class count the number of dimes in the first set. Have them make the same set with their dimes. Write the number in the box. Allow the children to complete the page independently.

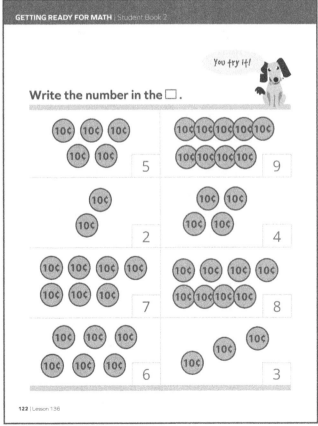

LESSON 137

MATERIALS NEEDED

• pencils
• addition and subtraction fact cards through 9
• number word cards

Objective:

To practice addition and subtraction facts through 9 in number symbols and number words, orally, vertically, and horizontally.

Teaching Pages 123 and 124:

1. Spend the first part of today's lesson reviewing the addition and subtraction facts. Make this an *oral quiz*. Read aloud from the fact cards *without showing them* to the students. State: "Four plus two equals ..." The student should respond, "Six." State: "Five minus zero equals ..." The student should respond, "Five." Continue this type of quiz. Allow the students objects for counting when they do not have the correct response. Before completing this exercise, have the children go through the number word cards once.

2. Turn to pages 123 and 124. Read the directions to each section with the students. Help them complete the first problem in each section. Be sure they read the operation symbol correctly. They may use the number word cards to complete the first set of exercises on each page. Allow them to complete the rest of the exercises independently.

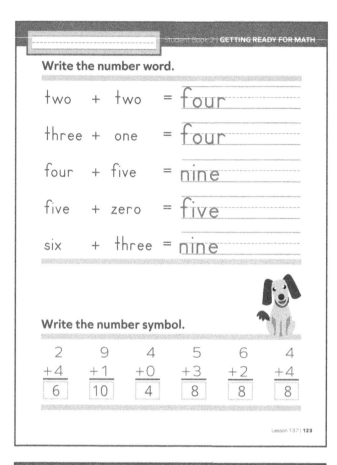

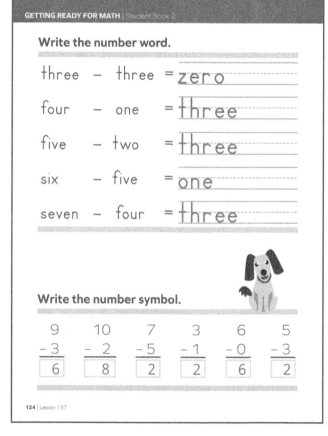

LESSON 138

MATERIALS NEEDED

- pencils
- pennies and dimes
- crayons through pink
- large and small objects

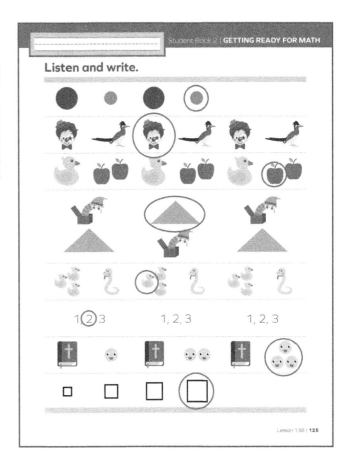

Listen and write.

Lesson 138 | 125

Objectives:

1. To learn patterns and sequencing.

2. To review ordinal (order) numbers.

3. To recognize shapes.

Teaching Pages 125 and 126:

1. Today's lesson develops the students' ability to recognize patterns and develop sequences. Use the pennies, dimes, crayons and other objects to develop some patterns for the students. After the students recognize the pattern, ask them to tell you what the next object would be in the sequence. Example: sequence of one penny, one dime, one penny, one dime, *or* sequence big, little, big, little, *or* sequence two pencils, one eraser, two pencils, one eraser. Continue with this until the students begin to understand the patterning and can tell the next number(s) or object(s) in the sequence.

2. Turn to page 125. Each line on this page represents a pattern of sequencing. Have the students identify the pattern and then tell, write, or draw what the next object(s) would be in the sequence.

     Row 1: big, little, big, little *or* purple, blue, purple, blue

     Row 2: clown, road runner, clown, road runner

     Row 3: duck, apples, duck, apples *or* 1, 2, 1, 2

     Row 4: over, under, over *or* under, over, under

     Row 5: ducks, snake, ducks, snake *or* 3, 1, 3, 1 *or* right, left, right, left

     Row 6: 1, 2, 3,   1, 2, 3,   1, 2, 3

     Row 7: Bible, smile(s), Bible, smiles *or* 1, 1, 1, 2, 1, 3

     Row 8: little to big

3. When you have finished talking about the patterns, tell the students to select a crayon and draw a circle around: 1) a *little* circle, 2) the *second* clown, 3) the *fifth* apple, 4) the triangle *over*

263

the jack-in-the-box, 5) the *fourth* duck, 6) the *first* number two, 7) the group of *three* smiling faces, and 8) the *biggest* square.

4. Draw an illustration of the four types of shapes the students have learned (circle, triangle, square, rectangle), and have them identify each one. Turn to page 126. Read the story at the top of the page, and have the children answer *Who am I?* Ask them to count the number of circles, triangles, squares, and rectangles that they find in the picture and write the numbers on the blank lines in the story (4, 2, 3, 4). Let them color the illustration using the colors they have learned.

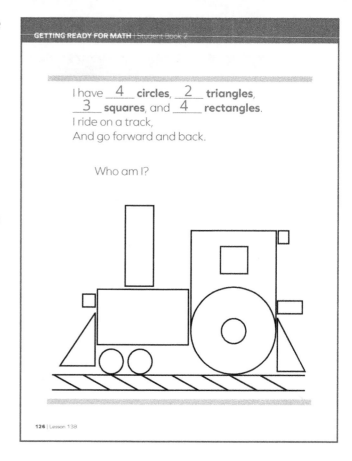

GETTING READY FOR MATH | Student Book 2

I have __4__ circles, __2__ triangles, __3__ squares, and __4__ rectangles.
I ride on a track,
And go forward and back.

Who am I?

126 | Lesson 138

LESSON 139

MATERIALS NEEDED

• pencils
• objects for counting

Objectives:

1. To write numbers to 50.

2. To write addition and subtraction facts in numbers and words horizontally.

3. To circle before and after.

4. To name the time, days of the week, and month.

Teaching Pages 127, 128, and 129:

1. Turn to page 127. Read the first set of directions, and give the students time to complete the exercise. Read the next set of directions, and allow the students to complete the page.

2. Turn to page 128. Follow the same procedure as 127.

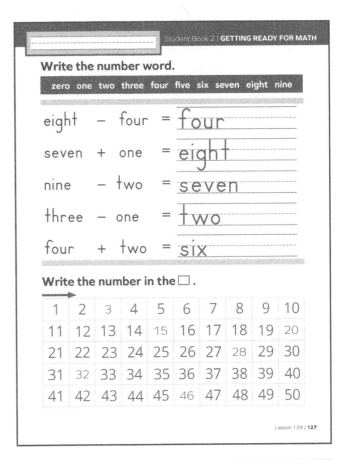

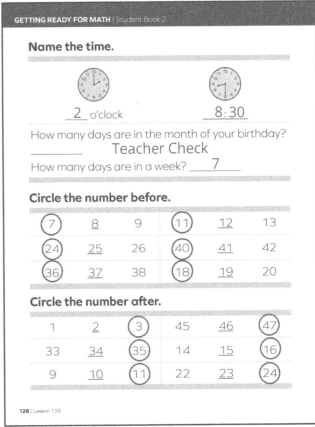

3. Turn to page 129. Follow the same procedure as 127 and 128.

4. Students may have objects for counting if necessary to complete the exercises. They should only refer to page 106 for counting if they are unable to complete the exercise.

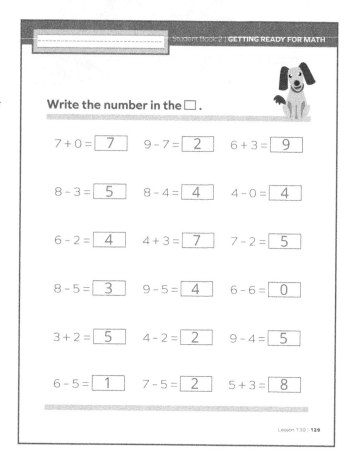

Student Book 2 | **GETTING READY FOR MATH**

Write the number in the ☐ .

$7 + 0 = \boxed{7}$ $9 - 7 = \boxed{2}$ $6 + 3 = \boxed{9}$

$8 - 3 = \boxed{5}$ $8 - 4 = \boxed{4}$ $4 - 0 = \boxed{4}$

$6 - 2 = \boxed{4}$ $4 + 3 = \boxed{7}$ $7 - 2 = \boxed{5}$

$8 - 5 = \boxed{3}$ $9 - 5 = \boxed{4}$ $6 - 6 = \boxed{0}$

$3 + 2 = \boxed{5}$ $4 - 2 = \boxed{2}$ $9 - 4 = \boxed{5}$

$6 - 5 = \boxed{1}$ $7 - 5 = \boxed{2}$ $5 + 3 = \boxed{8}$

Lesson 139 | **129**

LESSON 140

MATERIALS NEEDED

- pencils
- objects for counting

Objectives:

1. To write numbers to 50.

2. To write addition and subtraction facts in numbers and words horizontally.

3. To circle before and after.

4. To name the time, days of the week, and months.

Teaching Pages 130, 131, and 132:

1. Turn to page 130. Read the first set of directions, and give the students time to complete the exercise. Read the next set of directions, and allow the students to complete the page.

2. Turn to page 131. Follow the same procedure as 130.

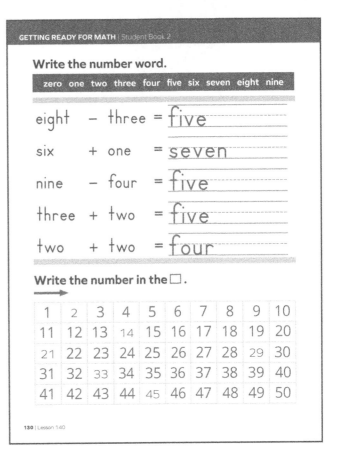

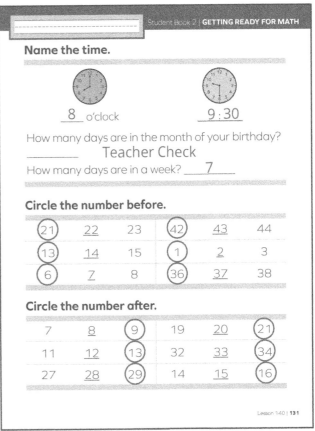

3. Turn to page 132. Follow the same procedure as 130 and 131.

4. Students may have objects for counting if necessary to complete the exercises. They should only refer to page 106 for counting if they are unable to complete the exercise.

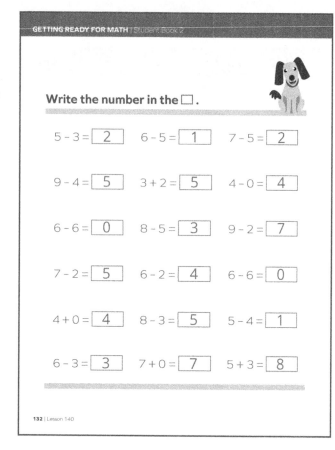

Write the number in the ☐ .

5 − 3 = 2	6 − 5 = 1	7 − 5 = 2
9 − 4 = 5	3 + 2 = 5	4 − 0 = 4
6 − 6 = 0	8 − 5 = 3	9 − 2 = 7
7 − 2 = 5	6 − 2 = 4	6 − 6 = 0
4 + 0 = 4	8 − 3 = 5	5 − 4 = 1
6 − 3 = 3	7 + 0 = 7	5 + 3 = 8

132 | Lesson 140

MATH KINDERGARTEN

Lessons 141–150

LESSON 141

MATERIALS NEEDED

- pencils
- objects for counting
- chart of numbers 1 to 50 from Lesson 131

Objectives:

1. To recognize number order.

2. To recognize the number that is greater or less.

Teaching Pages 133 and 134:

1. Have the children read the numbers on the chart of numbers *1* to *50* aloud.

2. Turn to page 133. Read the title of the page and review the definitions of greater and less with the children. Display ten items for the class to see. Make two sets of items (four items and six items). Have the children count the numbers in the sets. State, "Four is smaller than six. Four is less than six. Six is bigger than four. Six is greater than four."

Repeat this procedure using the numbers on page 133. Then have the children point to the answers as you ask these questions: "Which number is *greater*, 7 or 8? Which number is *less*, 5 or 6? Which number is *greater*, 14 or 15? Which number is *less*, 25 or 26?" Students may use the chart of numbers as an added reference. Use objects for counting as much as possible to develop the concept of the size of different numbers. Have the students complete the page by circling the correct number as you read.

Circle the number...

    1. that is greater. (43)
    2. that is less. (13)
    3. that is less. (2)
    4. that is greater. (31)
    5. that is less. (22)

NUMBER ORDER (GREATER, LESS)

Less (Smaller)		Greater (Bigger)
7	8 is greater than 7.	(8)
(5)	5 is less than 6.	6
14	15 is greater than 14.	(15)
(25)	25 is less than 26.	26

Circle the number.

42	(43)
(13)	14
(2)	3
30	(31)
(22)	23

Lesson 141 | **133**

3. Turn to page 134. Read the first set of instructions and point to the first pair of numbers, *5* and *6*. Have the children decide which is greater and circle it. (6) Allow the children to work as independently as possible. Have them use objects for counting and the chart of numbers. Read the second set of directions on page 134, and have the children proceed in the same manner but this time finding the number that is less.

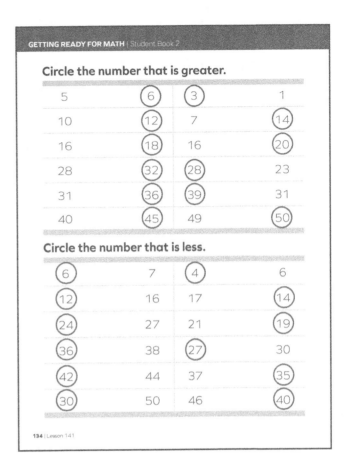

LESSON 142

MATERIALS NEEDED

- pencils
- objects for counting
- chart of numbers 1 to 50 from Lesson 131

Objectives:

1. To recognize number order.

2. To recall place value.

3. To recognize the number that is greater or less to 50.

Teaching Pages 135 and 136:

1. Have the students count aloud (without the chart of numbers) to *50*. Then show them the chart of numbers. Remind them that the number in the tens' place tells them how many sets of ten that the number represents. Help them decide if a number is *greater* or *less* by looking at the tens' place first and then the ones' place.

2. Turn to page 135. Read the first set of instructions with the students and point to the first pair of numbers, *6* and *8*. Ask which one is *less* and have them circle the *6*. Have them look at the *1* and *6* in the second column and tell which one is *greater*. Have them circle the *6*. Allow the children to work as independently as possible. Have them use objects for counting and the chart of numbers.

3. Turn to page 136 and have the children repeat the process for the first two exercises. Read the last set of directions. Students have a choice of several numbers to complete this exercise.

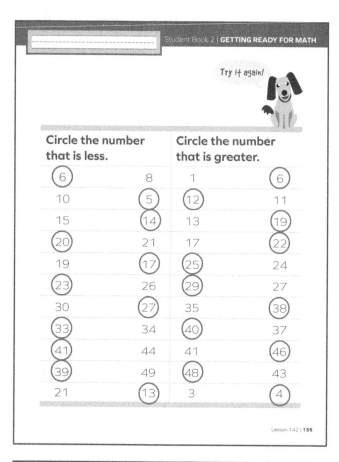

LESSON 143

MATERIALS NEEDED

- pencils
- objects for counting
- chart of numbers 1 to 50
- cardboard ($8\frac{1}{2} \times 11$ inches)
- scissors
- paste or glue

Objectives:

1. To count to 99.

2. To learn about place value for 10's and 1's.

Teaching Pages 137 and 138:

1. Turn to page 137. Read the title of the page and have the children count to 50 out loud, pointing to each number as they count. Tell the children to look at the numbers in the last column and point to the number in the tens' place. Talk about the sequence of *1, 2, 3, 4, 5*. Have them look at the last column in the second chart. Talk about the sequence of *6, 7, 8, 9*. Have the students continue counting from *51* to *99*. Have them point to each number as they count. Take time to repeat the procedure for students who are having difficulty.

2. Turn to page 138. Point to the number *1* in the first box. Tell the children to write the numbers in number order to *99*. Let the students use the chart of numbers *1* to *50* to begin the exercise, but they should try to complete it without looking at page 137. When page 138 is complete, cut out and paste page 137 to cardboard for a new chart of numbers *1* to *99*.

3. Have the students use the objects for counting to make sets of *10* through *90* in random order.

COUNT TO 99

You can count to 50!

1	2	3	4	5	6	7	8	9	10
11	12	13	14	15	16	17	18	19	20
21	22	23	24	25	26	27	28	29	30
31	32	33	34	35	36	37	38	39	40
41	42	43	44	45	46	47	48	49	50

Keep counting!

51	52	53	54	55	56	57	58	59	60
61	62	63	64	65	66	67	68	69	70
71	72	73	74	75	76	77	78	79	80
81	82	83	84	85	86	87	88	89	90
91	92	93	94	95	96	97	98	99	

Lesson 143 | **137**

Count to 99!

1	2	3	4	5	6	7	8	9	10
11	12	13	14	15	16	17	18	19	20
21	22	23	24	25	26	27	28	29	30
31	32	33	34	35	36	37	38	39	40
41	42	43	44	45	46	47	48	49	50
51	52	53	54	55	56	57	58	59	60
61	62	63	64	65	66	67	68	69	70
71	72	73	74	75	76	77	78	79	80
81	82	83	84	85	86	87	88	89	90
91	92	93	94	95	96	97	98	99	

138 | Lesson 143

LESSON 144

MATERIALS NEEDED

- pencils
- objects for counting
- new chart of numbers 1 to 99
- crayons—colors through pink

Objectives:

1. To write the number before and after to 90.

2. To count to 99.

Teaching Pages 139 and 140:

1. Have the children point to each number on the chart as they count aloud from *1* to *99*.

2. Do a *before* and *after* exercise with the children using objects for counting. When working with the larger numbers, arrange the objects in sets of *10's*. (37—three sets of tens plus seven objects) This will make it easier for the students to visualize the number *before* and the number *after*.

3. Turn to page 139. Read the directions, and have the students complete the page using their chart and objects for counting.

4. Turn to page 140. Call attention to the location of the *1*. Remind the children to count as they connect each dot. Ask the children if they think this is one of the animals that Noah took on the ark.

5. Read the nursery rhyme while the children color the illustration. Then, ask how many pigs are in the story.

> *This little pig went to market,*
> *this little pig stayed home,*
> *This little pig had roast beef,*
> *and this little pig had none,*
> *This little pig cried, "Wee, wee, wee"*
> *all the way home.*

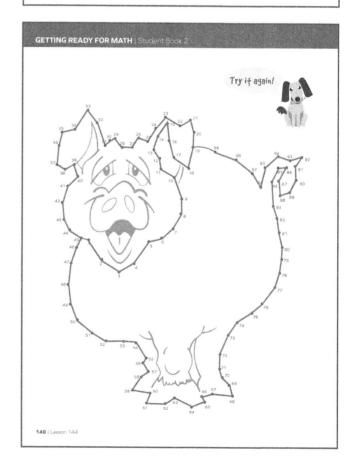

Student Book 2 | **GETTING READY FOR MATH**

Try it again!

Write the number.

before	9	8	after	6	7
before	13	12	after	15	16
before	21	20	after	67	68
before	57	56	after	21	22
before	40	39	after	79	80
before	36	35	after	32	33
before	86	85	after	37	38
before	17	16	after	93	94
before	29	28	after	49	50

Lesson 144 | **139**

GETTING READY FOR MATH | Student Book 2

Try it again!

140 | Lesson 144

LESSON 145

MATERIALS NEEDED

- pencils
- objects for counting
- chart of numbers 1 to 99

Objectives:

1. To review addition and subtraction facts, and to count to 99.

Teaching Pages 141 and 142:

1. Turn to page 141. Have the children read the first problem in the first column and ask them what they are supposed to do. (add) Tell them to write the answer in the box. Have the children read the first problem in the second column and ask them what they are supposed to do. (subtract) Tell them to write the answer in the box. Have them complete the page. Caution them to follow the signs carefully.

2. Turn to page 142. Tell the children that this time you will dictate the numbers from 1 to 99 while they write the number symbols in the box. Have the children raise their hands, clap, or somehow indicate when they come to a number already in the box. This will let you know whether the children are following the dictation correctly.

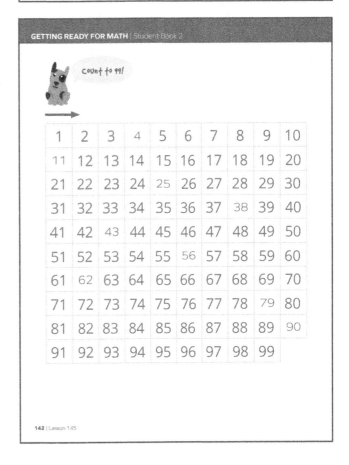

LESSON 146

MATERIALS NEEDED

- pencils
- objects for counting
- chart of numbers 1 to 99
- crayons—colors through pink

Objectives:

1. To skip count by 10's.

2. To solve story problems using illustrations.

Teaching Pages 143 and 144:

1. Turn to page 143. Have the children point to the chart and count from *1* to *10*. Ask them how many sets of ten this number represents. Ask them to make a set of ten using the objects for counting. Ask the children to count from *11* to *20*. Ask them how many sets of ten this number represents. Ask them to make a set of *20* (two sets of ten). Have them point to the *0* in the ones' place and the *2* in the tens' place. Have them point to the *30*. Ask them how many sets of ten this number represents. Have them make a set of *30* (three sets of ten). Have them point to the *0* in the ones' place and the *3* in the tens' place. Continue in this manner until you reach *90*. Have them count how many sets they have made. Ask them how many sets of ten make *90*. Tell them they can count by tens. Have them point to the numbers as they count *10, 20, 30, 40, 50, 60, 70, 80, 90*. Ask them again what each number represents (10 = one set of ten, 20 = two sets of ten, and so on). Have them count by tens, several times.

Student Book 2 | **GETTING READY FOR MATH**

Listen and write.

1	2	3	4	5	6	7	8	9	10
11	12	13	14	15	16	17	18	19	20
21	22	23	24	25	26	27	28	29	30
31	32	33	34	35	36	37	38	39	40
41	42	43	44	45	46	47	48	49	50
51	52	53	54	55	56	57	58	59	60
61	62	63	64	65	66	67	68	69	70
71	72	73	74	75	76	77	78	79	80
81	82	83	84	85	86	87	88	89	90
91	92	93	94	95	96	97	98	99	

Lesson 146 | **143**

2. Turn to page 144. Tell the children you are going to read a story to them and that they are supposed to illustrate the story. Tell them you will ask them a question about their illustration and they should write the number fact for the story. Ask the children to label their number facts. Objects may also be used to illustrate stories.

3. Story 1: Read the story. Have the students draw pictures of the three children. Have the students point to the first, second, and third in line. Show what would happen if Jane stepped out of line. (3 − 1 = 2)

4. Story 2: Read the story. Have the students draw pictures of the number of math pages that Linda finished on Monday and Tuesday. Have them add how many she completed altogether. (2 + 3 = 5)

5. Story 3: Read the story. Have the students draw the pieces of gum. Show what would happen if Jerry gave one piece to Larry. (4 − 1 = 3)

6. Story 4: Read the story. Have the students draw 6 apples and 2 apples. Have them decide which is the greater number of apples. Then answer the question. (6 is greater than 2.)

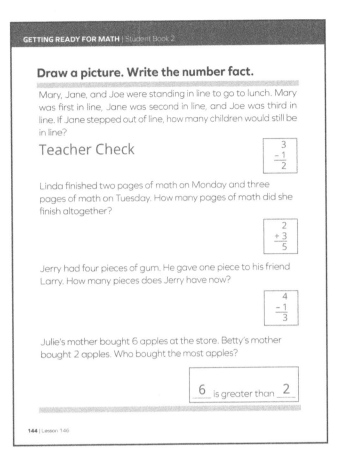

GETTING READY FOR MATH | Student Book 2

Draw a picture. Write the number fact.

Mary, Jane, and Joe were standing in line to go to lunch. Mary was first in line, Jane was second in line, and Joe was third in line. If Jane stepped out of line, how many children would still be in line?

Teacher Check

$$\begin{array}{r} 3 \\ -1 \\ \hline 2 \end{array}$$

Linda finished two pages of math on Monday and three pages of math on Tuesday. How many pages of math did she finish altogether?

$$\begin{array}{r} 2 \\ +3 \\ \hline 5 \end{array}$$

Jerry had four pieces of gum. He gave one piece to his friend Larry. How many pieces does Jerry have now?

$$\begin{array}{r} 4 \\ -1 \\ \hline 3 \end{array}$$

Julie's mother bought 6 apples at the store. Betty's mother bought 2 apples. Who bought the most apples?

_6_ is greater than _2_

144 | Lesson 146

LESSON 147

MATERIALS NEEDED

- pencils
- objects for counting
- chart of numbers 1 to 99

Objectives:

1. To skip count by 2's.

2. To find the number before and after to 99.

Teaching Pages 145 and 146:

1. Turn to page 145. Have the students look at the chart and review counting by *10*'s. Tell the children that today they will learn to count by *2*'s. Have them make five sets of objects with *2* objects in each set. Have them count the first set *1-2*, the second set *3-4*, the third set *5-6*, the fourth set *7-8*, the fifth set *9-10*. Next, tell the children to look at the chart on page 145. Have them point to *1* and *2* and count *1-2*. Have them circle the *2*. Have them point to the *3* and *4* and say, "I have counted two more numbers" and circle the *4*. Have them point to the *5* and *6* and say, "I have counted two more numbers" and circle the *6*. Continue in this manner to the *10*. Ask the children to read aloud the numbers that they have circled. Explain to them that this is called *counting by 2's*. Follow the same process to count by *2*'s through *20*. Some students may be able to continue on through *98*. Other students may do better by reviewing the process several times through *20*.

<table>
<tr><td>1</td><td>2</td><td>3</td><td>4</td><td>5</td><td>6</td><td>7</td><td>8</td><td>9</td><td>10</td></tr>
<tr><td>11</td><td>12</td><td>13</td><td>14</td><td>15</td><td>16</td><td>17</td><td>18</td><td>19</td><td>20</td></tr>
<tr><td>21</td><td>22</td><td>23</td><td>24</td><td>25</td><td>26</td><td>27</td><td>28</td><td>29</td><td>30</td></tr>
<tr><td>31</td><td>32</td><td>33</td><td>34</td><td>35</td><td>36</td><td>37</td><td>38</td><td>39</td><td>40</td></tr>
<tr><td>41</td><td>42</td><td>43</td><td>44</td><td>45</td><td>46</td><td>47</td><td>48</td><td>49</td><td>50</td></tr>
<tr><td>51</td><td>52</td><td>53</td><td>54</td><td>55</td><td>56</td><td>57</td><td>58</td><td>59</td><td>60</td></tr>
<tr><td>61</td><td>62</td><td>63</td><td>64</td><td>65</td><td>66</td><td>67</td><td>68</td><td>69</td><td>70</td></tr>
<tr><td>71</td><td>72</td><td>73</td><td>74</td><td>75</td><td>76</td><td>77</td><td>78</td><td>79</td><td>80</td></tr>
<tr><td>81</td><td>82</td><td>83</td><td>84</td><td>85</td><td>86</td><td>87</td><td>88</td><td>89</td><td>90</td></tr>
<tr><td>91</td><td>92</td><td>93</td><td>94</td><td>95</td><td>96</td><td>97</td><td>98</td><td>99</td><td></td></tr>
</table>

Student Book 2 | **GETTING READY FOR MATH**

Listen and write.

Lesson 147 | **145**

2. Turn to page 146. Read the directions to the first exercise with the children. Ask them to read the first problem in the first column, the first problem in the second column, and write the numbers. When you are sure they understand what they are to do, read the directions to the second exercise and have the students complete the first problem in each column. Be sure the children understand that there are exact answers to the first exercise, but there are several possible answers in the second exercise. They may use the chart of numbers if necessary.

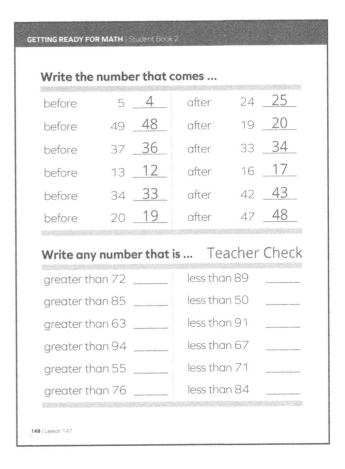

GETTING READY FOR MATH | Student Book 2

Write the number that comes ...

before	5	_4_	after	24	_25_
before	49	_48_	after	19	_20_
before	37	_36_	after	33	_34_
before	13	_12_	after	16	_17_
before	34	_33_	after	42	_43_
before	20	_19_	after	47	_48_

Write any number that is ...   Teacher Check

greater than 72	_____	less than 89	_____
greater than 85	_____	less than 50	_____
greater than 63	_____	less than 91	_____
greater than 94	_____	less than 67	_____
greater than 55	_____	less than 71	_____
greater than 76	_____	less than 84	_____

146 | Lesson 147

LESSON 148

MATERIALS NEEDED

- pencils
- objects for counting
- chart of numbers 1 to 99
- crayons—colors through pink

Objectives:

1. To skip count by 5's.

2. To illustrate counting by 2's.

Teaching Pages 147 and 148:

1. Turn to page 147. Have the students look at the chart and review counting by *10*'s and *2*'s. Tell the children that today they will learn to count by *5*'s. Have them make four sets of objects with 5 objects in each set. Have them count the first set *1-2-3-4-5*, the second set *6-7-8-9-10*, the third set *11-12-13-14-15*, the fourth set *16-17-18-19-20*. Next, tell the children to look at the chart on page 147. Have them point to *1-2-3-4-5* and count. Have them circle the *5*. Have them point to the *6-7-8-9-10* and say, "I have counted five more numbers" and circle the *10*. Have them point to the *11-12-13-14-15* and say, "I have counted five more numbers" and circle the *15*. Have them point to the *16-17-18-19-20* and say, "I have counted five more numbers" and circle the *20*. Ask the children to read the numbers that they have circled aloud. Explain to them that this is called counting by *5*'s. Follow the same process to count by *5*'s through *30*. Some students may be able to continue on through *95*. Other students may do better by reviewing the process several times through *30*.

Listen and write.

1	2	3	4	5	6	7	8	9	10
11	12	13	14	15	16	17	18	19	20
21	22	23	24	25	26	27	28	29	30
31	32	33	34	35	36	37	38	39	40
41	42	43	44	45	46	47	48	49	50
51	52	53	54	55	56	57	58	59	60
61	62	63	64	65	66	67	68	69	70
71	72	73	74	75	76	77	78	79	80
81	82	83	84	85	86	87	88	89	90
91	92	93	94	95	96	97	98	99	

Lesson 148 | **147**

2. Turn to page 148. Ask the children if this is an animal that Noah might have taken on the ark. Have them read the numbers *1-2, 3-4, 5-6, 7-8, 9-10*. Have them clap their hands as they say the second number. Then have them count *2-4-6-8-10*. Tell them to color the picture on page 148 while you read to them. Then, tell them to repeat the nursery rhyme with you.

> *One-two, buckle my shoe;*
> *Three-four, shut the door;*
> *Five-six, pick up sticks;*
> *Seven-eight, lay them straight;*
> *Nine-ten, a big fat hen.*

GETTING READY FOR MATH | Student Book 2

Count by 2's.

1, **2,**

3, **4,**

5, **6,**

7, **8,**

9, **10**

148 | Lesson 148

LESSON 149

MATERIALS NEEDED

• pencils
• objects for counting

Objectives:

1. To make sets to illustrate number facts.

2. To write number facts.

Teaching Pages 149 and 150:

1. Turn to page 149. Read the directions and have the children write the number words. Read the second set of directions. Have the students use the objects for counting to make the sets and then write the answer as a number word on the line.

2. Turn to page 150. Read the directions and have the children write the number symbols from *0* to *20*. Read the first set of directions and have the students complete the exercise using objects for counting and then writing the answer. Read the last set of directions. Notice that in this set the students are to write three number facts of their own choosing.

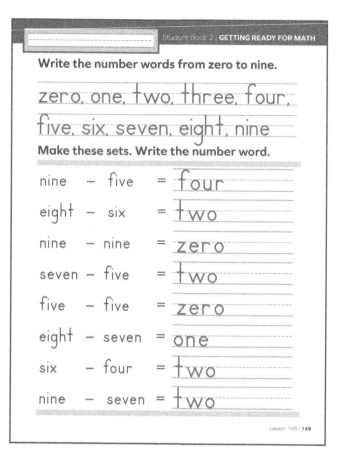

Student Book 2 | GETTING READY FOR MATH

Write the number words from zero to nine.

zero, one, two, three, four,
five, six, seven, eight, nine

Make these sets. Write the number word.

nine	–	five	=	four
eight	–	six	=	two
nine	–	nine	=	zero
seven	–	five	=	two
five	–	five	=	zero
eight	–	seven	=	one
six	–	four	=	two
nine	–	seven	=	two

Lesson 149 | **149**

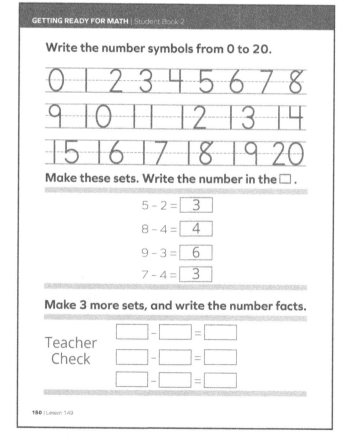

GETTING READY FOR MATH | Student Book 2

Write the number symbols from 0 to 20.

0 1 2 3 4 5 6 7 8
9 10 11 12 13 14
15 16 17 18 19 20

Make these sets. Write the number in the ☐.

5 – 2 = 3
8 – 4 = 4
9 – 3 = 6
7 – 4 = 3

Make 3 more sets, and write the number facts.

Teacher
Check

☐ – ☐ = ☐
☐ – ☐ = ☐
☐ – ☐ = ☐

150 | Lesson 149

LESSON 150

MATERIALS NEEDED

- pencils
- objects for counting
- yellow, purple, and orange crayons

Objectives:

1. To write the number of the hour.

2. To add a number to 10.

3. To count with words to 9.

4. To add and subtract number facts.

5. To count in symbols to 20.

Teaching Pages 151 and 152:

1. Turn to page 151. Read each set of instructions out loud. Have someone in the class tell the story of Jacob's ladder or read it aloud (Genesis 28:10–17). Tell the children to write the number words in order going up Jacob's ladder. Allow the students to complete the page independently.

2. Turn to page 152. Read the instructions and tell the children to complete the number facts. Be sure they are reading the sign and understand where to add and where to subtract. Have them write the numbers in number order in the ovals. Tell them to use their yellow crayon to circle the numbers as they count by *10* (10-20), use their purple crayon to circle the numbers as they count by *2* (2-4-6), and their orange crayon to circle as they count by *5* (5-10-15-20).

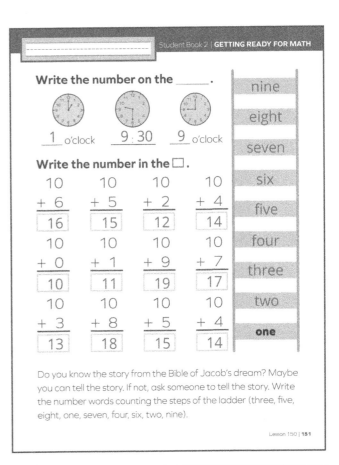

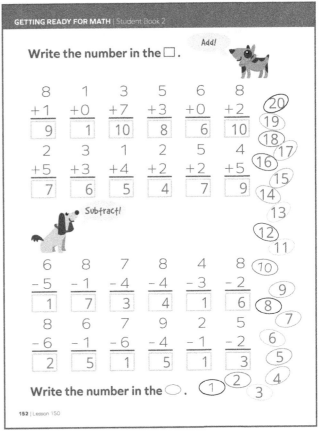

283

MATH KINDERGARTEN

Lessons 151–160

LESSON 151

MATERIALS NEEDED

- pencils
- paper
- pennies

Objective:

To add pennies.

Teaching Pages 153 and 154:

1. Turn to page 153 and read the title of the page. Show a penny to the class and state, "This object is money. We call it a penny." (Write *penny* on the board or on paper.) "We can call it *one cent*." (Write *1¢* and *one cent* on the board or paper.) "We use the words *pennies*, *cents*, and the sign *¢* when we are talking about money." Have the children point to the number fact *1¢ + 3¢ = 4¢*. Read it out loud. Ask them what the plus sign is telling them to do. (add) Repeat this procedure with each of the remaining number facts. Give the children pennies. Have the children make up sets of pennies, add them, and write the corresponding number facts on a piece of paper.

2. Turn to page 154. Read the instructions out loud. Add the first number fact together as a class. Allow the children to complete the page independently. Check the children periodically as they complete their work.

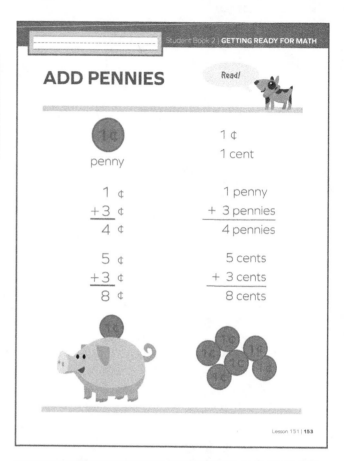

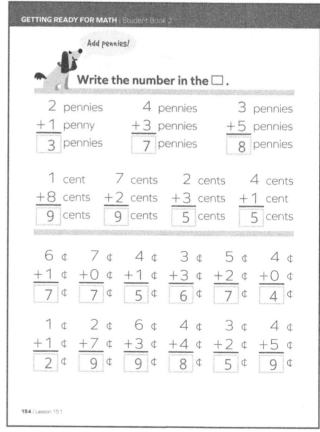

LESSON 152

MATERIALS NEEDED

- pencils
- paper
- pennies and dimes

Objectives:

1. To show how dimes equal pennies.

2. To learn to add dimes.

Teaching Pages 155 and 156:

1. Turn to page 155 and read the title of the page. Show a dime to the class and state, "This object is money. We call it a dime." (Write *dime* on the board or on paper.) "We can call it *ten cents*." Tell the children to make a pile of ten pennies. Give the dime to them and say, "This dime is equal to the ten pennies." Have the students make another pile of ten pennies. Ask them how many dimes are equal to the two piles of ten pennies. (two dimes) Ask them why we need dimes. (We would need to carry too many pennies in our pockets.) Write *10¢* and *ten cents* on the board or paper. Hold a dime up in front of the children and explain to them that we may express a dime on paper two ways. We may write *1 dime* or *10¢*. Have the children use the pennies and dimes to illustrate that one dime, two dimes, three dimes, and four dimes are equal to ten cents, twenty cents, thirty cents, and forty cents. Have the children point to the number fact *10¢ + 30¢ = 40¢*. Read it out loud. Ask the children what the plus sign is telling them to do. (add) Have them illustrate the number fact with the play money. Continue this procedure with each of the remaining number facts. Give the children play dimes. Have the children make up sets of dimes, add them, and write the corresponding number facts on a piece of paper. Show the facts as dimes and then as cents.

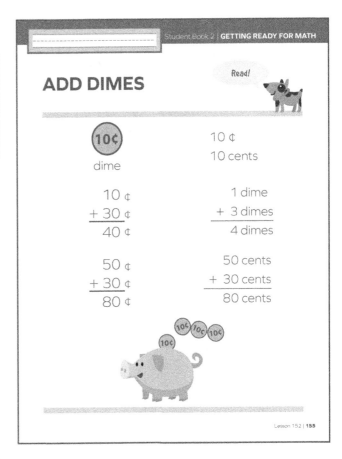

2. Turn to page 156 and read the instructions out loud. Add the first number fact together as a class. Ask the students to illustrate each number fact with the money.

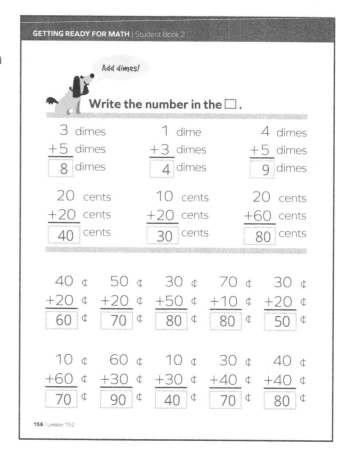

LESSON 153

MATERIALS NEEDED

- pencils
- cardboard
- crayons through pink
- scissors
- paste or glue

Objective:

To count pennies and dimes.

Teaching Pages 157 and 158:

1. Turn to page 157. Read the instructions out loud.

2. Turn to page 158. Have the children make the piggy banks. Tell the children to cut out the pennies and dimes. Tell them to write the number of pennies (8), the number of dimes (5), and their names on the banks.

Instructions for page 158: Make piggy banks.

- Color the piggy banks.
- Cut out the piggy banks.
- Paste or glue the pigs to the cardboard along the solid line.
- Do not paste along the dotted line.
- Cut the cardboard the same shape as the piggy banks.

- Cut out each penny and paste or glue to the cardboard.
- Cut out the cardboard in the same shape as the penny.
- Count the pennies and write the number on the piggy bank.
- Put each penny in the piggy bank.

- Cut out each dime and paste or glue to the cardboard.
- Cut out the cardboard in the same shape as the dime.
- Count the dimes and write the number on the piggy bank.
- Put each dime in the piggy bank.

Lesson 153 | **157**

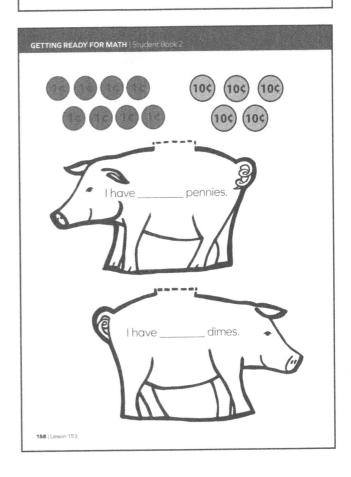

I have _____ pennies.

I have _____ dimes.

158 | Lesson 153

LESSON 154

MATERIALS NEEDED

- pencils
- cardboard
- yellow, brown, and red crayons
- scissors
- paste or glue
- pennies and dimes

Objective:

To count pennies and dimes.

Teaching Pages 159 and 160:

1. Turn to page 159. Read the instructions out loud. Have the children read the problem aloud, illustrate the problem with money, and then write the answer in the box. Be sure the children understand that the ¢ sign represents cents or pennies.

2. Turn to page 160. Dictate the numbers while the children write in the boxes. Have them raise their hands or indicate when you reach a number already in a box. Place a group of *10* objects and the yellow crayon in front of the students. Tell them to count the objects and then circle the number that this set represents. Place another group of *10* objects in front of the students and ask, "How many now?" (20) Have them circle the *20* on the number chart. Have the children continue counting by *10*'s and circling the numbers on the chart (30, 40, 50, 60, 70, 80, 90). Give the brown crayon to the students, have them count by *5*'s, circling the number on the chart as they count. Give the red crayon to the students and have them repeat the same process counting by *2*'s.

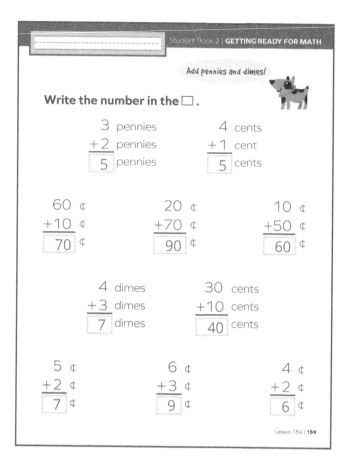

LESSON 155

MATERIALS NEEDED

- pencils
- chart of numbers to 99

Objectives:

1. To write number words and number facts.

2. To tell numbers before, after, and between.

Teaching Pages 161 and 162:

1. Turn to page 161 and read the directions at the top of the page aloud. Have the children point to the lines. Dictate the number words *zero* through *nine* to the children while they write them on the lines. Read the second set of directions. Tell the children that you will dictate four number facts to them and that they should write the number facts in the boxes. Tell them to write neatly, to write the correct sign, and to remember to draw the line between the problem and the answer.
   Dictate: Six minus two equals four.

$$\begin{array}{cccc} 6 & 9 & 4 & 7 \\ -2 & -6 & +5 & +1 \\ \hline 4 & 3 & 9 & 8 \end{array}$$

2. Turn to page 162. Read the first direction and have the children point to the first number. (9) Tell them to find the number on their number chart and say aloud the number that is before and the number after. Have them write the numbers on the lines. Read the second set of directions. Have the children point to the first set of numbers (7–9). Tell them to find the numbers on their number chart and say aloud the number that is between. Have them write the number on the line. Read the third direction and have the students find *19* on the number chart, then have them write the number after. Those students who understand the directions may complete the page independently. Others may require help as they complete each section.

Student Book 2 | **GETTING READY FOR MATH**

Write the number words.

zero, one, two, three,
four, five, six, seven,
eight, nine

Write the number facts.

$$\begin{array}{cc} \quad 6 & \quad 9 \\ -2 & -6 \\ \hline 4 & 3 \end{array}$$

$$\begin{array}{cc} \quad 4 & \quad 7 \\ +5 & +1 \\ \hline 9 & 8 \end{array}$$

Lesson 155 | **161**

GETTING READY FOR MATH | Student Book 2

Write the number before and the after.

_8_	9	_10_	_52_	53	_54_
_23_	24	_25_	_66_	67	_68_
_37_	38	_39_	_77_	78	_79_
_48_	49	_50_	_81_	82	_83_

Write the number between.

7	_8_	9	56	_57_	58
14	_15_	16	62	_63_	64
27	_28_	29	87	_88_	89
30	_31_	32	95	_96_	97

Write the number.

after 19	_20_	before 60	_59_
before 30	_29_	after 71	_72_
after 42	_43_	after 89	_90_
after 59	_60_	before 99	_98_

162 | Lesson 155

LESSON 156

MATERIALS NEEDED

- pencils
- objects of various sizes
- chart of numbers to 99
- crayons—colors through pink

Objectives:

1. To tell numbers greater than and less than to 99.
2. To follow directions.

Teaching Pages 163 and 164:

1. Place several different sets in front of the students, and ask which is bigger and which is smaller. Use the expressions *greater than* and *less than* so the children become familiar with these terms. Point to the numbers on the number chart. Ask the children about the order of the numbers (small to large). Point to several numbers on the number chart and ask which one is *greater than* or *less than* the other.
2. Turn to page 163. Read the directions to the children. Have them complete this page by finding the numbers on the number chart and then circling the correct answer. Remind them to look for place value of tens and ones.
3. Turn to page 164. Give the children a minute to look at the picture and identify some of the objects. Then state: "Point to the sun *above* the mountain, the tail *below* the kite, the tail *beside* the cat, the cloud to the *right* of the sun, the butterfly to the *left* of the cat, a *big* flower, a *little* flower." Read the directions at the bottom of the page. Tell the children to color the pictures using the colors shown in the directions. They may finish coloring the picture using colors of their own choosing.

Student Book 2 | **GETTING READY FOR MATH**

Circle the number that is less.

9	⑧	63	㊴
㉟	49	54	⑫
18	⑫	(57)	62
⑬	20	53	㊽
㊷	47	39	㉛
21	⑰	㊾	50

Circle the number that is greater.

16	㉓	(91)	62
(84)	72	㊴	32
6	⑱	29	㉛
28	㉙	(76)	75
42	㊹	㊲	35
30	㊿	㊻	40

Lesson 156 | 163

GETTING READY FOR MATH | Student Book 2

Listen and find. Teacher Check

Color

red – kite	brown – mountain
yellow – sun	purple – flower
blue – sky	pink – flower
green – grass	black – shoes
orange – cat	white – clouds, snow

164 | Lesson 156

LESSON 157

MATERIALS NEEDED

- pencils
- various types of objects
- chart of numbers to 99

Objectives:

1. To write number words and number facts.

2. To tell numbers before, after, and between.

3. To recognize patterns and sequence.

Teaching Pages 165 and 166:

1. Turn to page 165. Read the directions to the students. (The children should not use the chart of numbers unless they are unable to complete the assignment without it.) When the children have written all of the numbers, have them skip count by *10's, 2's,* and *5's.* Have them point to the numbers as they count.

count to 99!

1	2	3	4	5	6	7	8	9	10
11	12	13	14	15	16	17	18	19	20
21	22	23	24	25	26	27	28	29	30
31	32	33	34	35	36	37	38	39	40
41	42	43	44	45	46	47	48	49	50
51	52	53	54	55	56	57	58	59	60
61	62	63	64	65	66	67	68	69	70
71	72	73	74	75	76	77	78	79	80
81	82	83	84	85	86	87	88	89	90
91	92	93	94	95	96	97	98	99	

Lesson 157 | **165**

2. Ask the children if they remember finding patterns in Lesson 138. If necessary, review page 125. Use objects to make some patterns. Have the children describe the patterns and tell what would be the next object in the sequence. Ask the students to make some of their own patterns.

3. Turn to page 166. Tell the children that there is a pattern to each one of the exercises. Work with them on each exercise to develop the correct response. Have them write or draw the next number(s) or object(s) in the sequence.

Row 1: count by 2's (8)

Row 2: inside, outside *or* outside, inside (circle in a square)

Row 3: big, little *or* 1, 2, 1, 2 (2 little houses)

Row 4: count by 10's (40)

Row 5: up, down (apple up)

Row 6: car, dog *or* right, left (car facing right)

Row 7: count by 5's (20)

Row 8: add one more in alphabetical order (a, b, c, d, e)

GETTING READY FOR MATH | Student Book 2

Listen and write.   Teacher Check

1. 2, 4, 6, ___8___

2.

3.

4. 10, 20, 30, ___40___

5.

6.

7. 5, 10, 15, ___20___

8. ab, abc, abcd, ___abcde___

166 | Lesson 157

LESSON 158

MATERIALS NEEDED

- pencils
- objects for counting
- paper
- pennies and dimes

Objectives:

1. To write numbers in the ones' and tens' place.

2. To tell how many dimes and how many pennies.

Teaching Pages 167 and 168:

1. Place a group of *14* objects in front of the students. Have them count the objects and then ask them to divide the objects into sets of ten (1 set of ten plus 4 objects). Have the students write *14* on a piece of paper. Point out the *1* in the tens' place and the *4* in the ones' place. Repeat the process using the numbers *26* and *54*.

Write how many tens, how many ones.

	tens	ones
12	1	2
35	3	5
42	4	2
76	7	6
85	8	5

Write how many dimes, how many pennies.

	dimes	pennies
15¢	1	5
23¢	2	3
38¢	3	8
57¢	5	7
85¢	8	5

Lesson 158 | **167**

2. Turn to page 167 and read the first set of directions to the children. Point to the columns for tens and ones. Ask the children to write how many sets of tens in the number *12* (1) and how many ones (2). Have the children complete the first exercise. Those children who have difficulty should continue using objects for counting to make sets of tens and sets of ones.

3. Show the children a dime and ask what it represents. (a set of ten pennies) Give the children *15* pennies and have them count them. Tell them to separate the pennies into sets of tens (1) and ones (5). Ask the children what they can use in place of the set of ten pennies. (one dime) Repeat the process using *35¢* and *62¢*. Read the second set of directions on page 167 to the children. Have them write how many dimes and how many pennies. Continue with the dimes and pennies as necessary.

4. Turn to page 168. Identify each one of the objects, and ask the children what the yellow tags are for. Ask the students to say the amount on each tag aloud. Read the directions and have the students complete the page. They may use their dimes and pennies to "buy" the objects from the store.

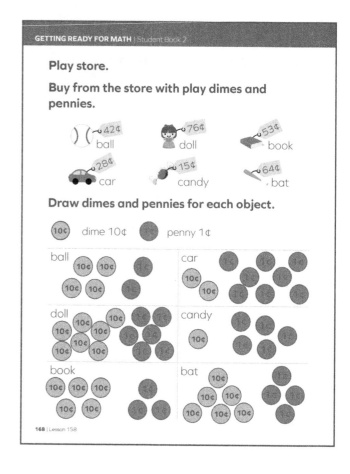

LESSON 159

MATERIALS NEEDED

- pencils
- chart of numbers to 99
- crayons—colors through pink

Objectives:

1. To tell time to the hour and half-hour.

2. To tell the days of the week from the calendar.

3. To write numbers in number order.

4. To count how many.

5. To write addition and subtraction facts.

Teaching Pages 169, 170, and 171:

1. Turn to page 169 and read the first set of directions. Have the children complete the section. Read the second set of directions. Ask the children what the next illustration looks like. (calendar) Ask them to name as many months as they can. Tell them this calendar is for the month of June, and have them write *June* and the current year above the calendar. Ask them what is the first number and the last number on the calendar. (1 and 30) Tell them to fill in the missing numbers. Point out the days of the week at the top of the calendar and read them aloud with the children. Read the last set of directions, and have the students write the correct day of the week on each line.

2. Turn to page 170. Ask the students to identify the figures, and then read the first set of directions. The children may complete this section independently. They may use the chart of numbers if necessary. Read the second set of directions. Have the children draw faces starting with a circle and using a square or triangle and a straight line for a hat. Remind them to put eyes, noses, smiles, and ears on the faces. Then have the children count the total number of

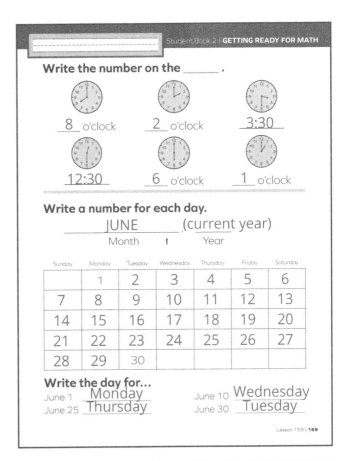

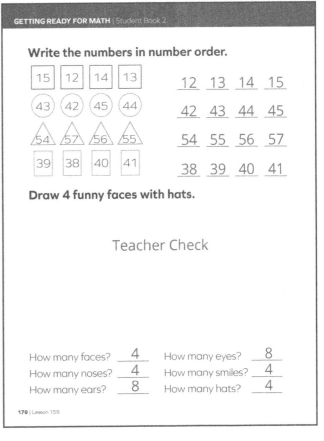

faces, eyes, noses, smiles, ears, and hats, and write the answer on the line.

3. Turn to page 171. Read the directions and point out the plus (+) and minus (−) signs to the children. Allow them to complete the page independently.

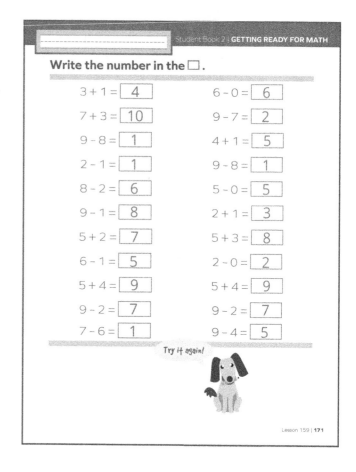

Student Book 2 | **GETTING READY FOR MATH**

Write the number in the □ .

3 + 1 = 4	6 − 0 = 6
7 + 3 = 10	9 − 7 = 2
9 − 8 = 1	4 + 1 = 5
2 − 1 = 1	9 − 8 = 1
8 − 2 = 6	5 − 0 = 5
9 − 1 = 8	2 + 1 = 3
5 + 2 = 7	5 + 3 = 8
6 − 1 = 5	2 − 0 = 2
5 + 4 = 9	5 + 4 = 9
9 − 2 = 7	9 − 2 = 7
7 − 6 = 1	9 − 4 = 5

Try it again!

Lesson 159 | **171**

LESSON 160

MATERIALS NEEDED

- pencils
- chart of numbers to 99
- a group of large and small objects
- crayons—colors through pink

Objectives:

1. To tell what is greater than to 99.

2. To solve story problems.

3. To write addition and subtraction facts.

Teaching Pages 172, 173, and 174:

1. Place the objects in sets of one large and one small. Ask the children to point to the set that is greater than (or less than) the other set. When the students are familiar with the expression greater than, have them turn to page 172. Ask the children to identify the illustrations and say the numbers aloud. Read the directions. Allow the students to complete the page independently.

2. Turn to page 173. Tell the children that you are going to tell them some stories and then ask them questions. They may draw pictures of the stories and then write number facts for their answers.

   1. Draw a picture of five cookies and show what happens if you eat two. (5 − 2 = 3)

   2. Draw a picture of four blocks one on top of the other. Add one more block. (4 + 1 = 5)

   3. Draw a tree with six birds and then show four flying away. (6 − 4 = 2)

   4. Draw illustrations of two sets of stairs. (4 and 6) Tell which is greater. (6 is greater than 4.)

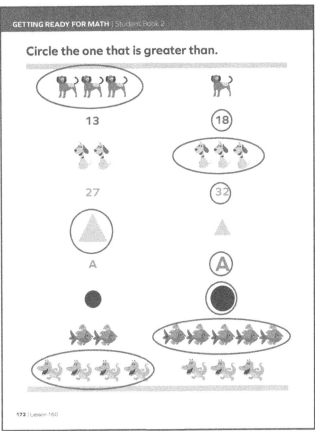

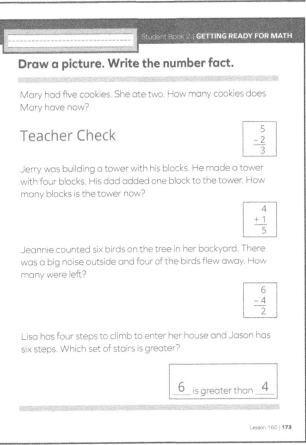

3. Turn to page 174. Read the directions and point out the plus (+) and minus (−) signs to the children. Allow them to complete the page independently.

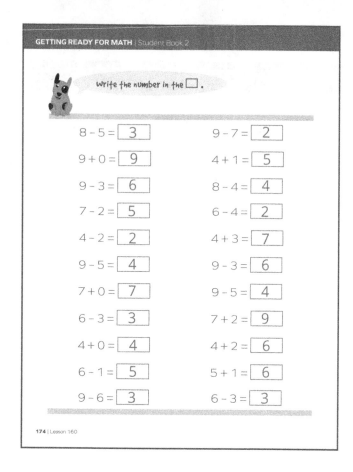